SMILING
WATER

Mair Winfield

First Impression—1999

ISBN 1 85902 742 3

This book is published with the support of the
Arts Council of Wales.

Printed in Wales at
Gomer Press, Llandysul, Ceredigion

This book is dedicated
to the memory of my parents;
my brother, Daniel
and my very dear friend
Mrs J. D. Staley.

PROLOGUE

1980

Thursday assemblies were always special in Yorkswood. It was the time when we gave thanks for all the good things in life and tried to put right any problems that had arisen during the week. Today in our service, we had endeavoured to apologise to our caretaker Mrs Mortimore for last week's transgressions – untidy classrooms and messy toilets – and express our gratitude for all her hard work.

I walked into the now empty assembly hall. The paintings, collages and writing presented in this morning's assembly were already mounted and displayed on the orange screen with the appropriate captions. I stood in front of a large collage picture of our red-cheeked cleaning lady, surrounded by floating white angels carrying mops and buckets and underneath, the prayer:

> Please God send your angels to help our caretaker Mrs Mortimore clean our messy toilets.

How Jinny would have loved this morning's service! I could almost hear her chuckle, 'Good God, gel, you sure do pick 'em!'

In my two headships I had been privileged to know two exceptional caretakers, dedicated workaholics, unforgettable characters each with her own special brand of humour. It was strange that news of Jinny's death this morning had coincided with our special service and the 'phone call had affected me deeply.

However, in a school such as Yorkswood, on a large Birmingham council estate, where each day brought its own challenges, problems and decisions, personal emotions had to be suppressed and 'Press on regardless' had to be our motto.

Now at the end of the day, I had peace to think and grieve for Jinny and remember those years in Gwenddwr.

1

1951

I climbed on to the high bed and as I sank into the deep feathered mattress, I felt the warmth of the rubber bottle at my feet and the cold, clean, white sheets under my chin. From plumped up feather-filled pillows, I stared about me.

The flickering lights of the candle on the bedside table to my left created dancing shadows on the brown and creamy leaf patterns on the wallpaper. A starched white runner, edged with lace, covered the large chest of drawers in front of me, and above on the wall, in a dark wooden frame, was an embroidered text. The long oval mirror on the wardrobe to my right, reflected a still-life image of the glowing china jug and basin, which stood opposite on the marble-topped washing stand near the creaky painted door.

I lay there in that strange bed feeling desolate and alone. For comfort, I snuggled under the heavy blankets and the fluffy yellow candlewick bedspread; then the emotion and grief of the preceding months and the events which had led me here, came rushing back.

The candle was now burning steadily and the flame illuminated the text on the wall.

> God is our shelter and strength
> always ready to help in times of trouble.

Why was I here? Was this God's way of helping me in my time of trouble? What strange force had pushed me to apply for a teaching post that brought me to this remote village at the foot of the Epynt mountain?

I was married in April 1947 and the memory of blossom time that year would always remain with me.

9

We had taken a first floor flat with a large bay window that overlooked two spreading almond trees, which spanned the width of the front garden. It seemed to me in my misery that the mass of thick, pink blossom was threateningly poised outside that large pane of glass, ready to tumble in and suffocate me. I was a bride of a few weeks only, but already living a life that had become a nightmare. I was too young, too immature to deal with a situation which was beyond my comprehension.

I had known him from Grammar School days – a head prefect and captain of the rugger team who had volunteered for Air-Crew; everybody's hero. To everyone else, I was the lucky one married to a Squadron Leader D.F.C., all set to begin a promising university career in Bristol.

'A good catch,' they'd said as they crowded around Rhys the photographer's window. Could that radiant young bride in the wedding album really be me? In the family group everyone looked so happy! Even my Auntie Annie, who could always be relied on to have a sense of foreboding, had a big smile on her face. Wasn't there the slightest doubt in anyone's mind?

There were periods of happiness – yes! I was grateful for every kind word, every smile and every gesture of affection, but the unpredictable moods, the violence and depression became a regular pattern of behaviour and together we shared a private hell in that bed-sitting room that overlooked the blossom trees.

I don't know when I consciously decided to submit and accept my fate. In any case, I came to realise that even though physically he had come through the war unscathed, my husband was scarred by the experiences of war and the bombing missions had become part of his nightmares. I had no contact with anyone who could give me advice and he would never accept that he needed help.

We were together for four years and we had two daughters, Sharon and Lynne, but that gave no stability or permanence to our relationship. I knew instinctively that it was only a matter of time.

I was to see him graduate, but the Easter he found a teaching post in London, he told me he was leaving us. He could no longer face the pressures and responsibilities of family life. We were staying with his parents at the time, and on that last day we had tea in the cottage garden near the station.

'Don't come down to the train,' he said.

From the distance came the far-off whistle of the train. He went down the garden path with quick, heavy footsteps, through the arched gateway and on to the winding road that dipped, hiding the platform from view.

The thin, hot tea scalded my throat as I gulped nervously, trying hard to control the panic which seemed to have a paralysing effect on my mind and body. I was acutely aware of the setting, as if I were on the outside looking in – a figure sitting in solitude, in a garden full of daffodils and purple aubretia. From the window boxes wafted the sickly sweet scent of the pink and blue hyacinths which I thereafter was to associate with a sinking feeling in the pit of my stomach. In a daze I heard the approaching train, the squeal of brakes, the slamming doors and the chug-chugging of the train as it carried him out of our lives for ever.

We went home, the children and I. Home was a school house in Gwynfe, a village at the foot of the Black Mountains where my father was the local schoolmaster.

After the initial shock, which naturally caused dismay and distress, came love and support from my parents and my brother Daniel. And so there were weeks of weeping and I would wander over the fields carrying Lynne in my arms and Sharon trailing behind.

Kahlil Gibran wrote:

And a woman spoke saying, 'Tell us of pain',

And he said:

Your pain is the breaking of the shell that encloses your understanding. Even as the stone of the fruit must break that its heart may stand in the sun, so must you know pain.

So it was with me. During our four years together, I had suffered greatly but at the final parting I was overwhelmed with grief, and I could not accept that this was the end. The months went by and there was still no letter. Then it was July and his

11

birthday. I sent a card and a gift from the children and me. It was returned with the note,

'I want nothing from you or yours.'

At last, I sought psychiatric advice and was told, 'In cases like this they often turn against the ones they love the most. If he will not accept that he needs help, then let him go.'

How then should I feel? Compassion for him because he was not responsible for his actions? How much easier it would be, to be able to feel bitter and angry.

2

Summer was soon gone and autumn was already here but I was still oblivious to the seasonal changes around me. I was wallowing in my own misery.

> Much of your pain is self chosen. It is the bitter potion, by which the physician within you heals your sick self.
>
> (Kahlil Gibran)

It happened suddenly – the healing, I mean. As if the black cloud which engulfed me for so long was lifting. I woke up early on that October morning. Lynne was sound asleep in her cot and Sharon was curled up beside me.

The early morning sun shone on my face and outside my bedroom window the greenish black branches of the old apple tree stood out stark and clear. How often I had sat in its solid boughs reciting from Shakespeare; memorising my Latin declensions; working out chemical equations and learning about Amoeba and Chlamydomonas. It had served as my 'cwtch', my snug, during Grammar School days.

I had a strong urge to be out in the fresh early morning breeze, so quickly and quietly in slacks and a warm woolly sweater, I let myself out through the back door into the untidy, friendly lane called Hewl Fach that ran alongside our garden hedge. Then on, down to that sprawling sloping meadow called Gellicaerau, the favourite haunt of my childhood.

I walked with sprightly step. The lane was alive with colour – the dabbed autumn hedgerows, the bending hawthorn trees laden with clusters of rich red haws, the rose hips swaying elegantly in the morning air and the rich blue sloes clinging to the blackthorn. I had been blind for so long and now with restored sight, I was acutely aware of every shape and every colour. On reaching the gate at the end of Hewl Fach I was

13

once more confronted with the rolling magnificence of my beloved Black Mountain – Y Mynydd Du.

As always, in spite of the expansive green meadows and the yellow stubbled wheat fields that tumbled down the slopes, those rounded grave hills seemed only a stone's throw away.

As a child I would call out to those echoing hills, '*Dere ma!*' (Come here!) and I thought I had found a playmate. Suddenly I had the urge to cry out again to my beloved Mynydd Du, – 'I am here and I am alive again!'

The remembrance of all those childhood pleasures were reawakened. I had so much to share with Sharon and Lynne.

At the bottom of Gellicaerau there is a copse where the hazel trees at that time of the year would be laden with ripe brown nuts and we would shake them down. The long, sharply-spiked yellow gorse where badgers lurked, still covered the sloping land to my left, hiding from sight the secret lane where in spring, yellow primroses mingled with violets and wild sorrel.

In the field beyond the lane ran a rippling stream rich in trout, where my brother Daniel and I had spent happy hours, knee-deep in the crystal clear water and with our hands, catching and tickling the slippery fish that had sought shelter under the large, flat stones.

From Gellicaerau I looked down at Brynchwith Farm in the valley to my right and Glantoddeb and Ynystoddeb to my left. We had spent such happy times there. They were our kind neighbours and always at hand whenever they were needed. Since returning home I had avoided contact with friends and relatives. I just wanted to hide from the outside world, and I was grateful to everyone for respecting my need for privacy. I knew too that the gifts of milk, butter and eggs which people brought to the school house was their way of showing their support.

From the other side of the Black Mountain on the once weekly local bus on Fridays, came Auntie Hetty, Auntie Mary, Auntie Dora and Auntie Annie, all with love in their faces and full of pity for me.

Having stayed away for an accepted period of time they were all full of advice and already planning my future.

14

'Of course you will go back to teaching . . .'

'Mam and Dada would look after the children . . .'

'Isnt it very likely that there will be a vacancy in your father's school? How lucky!'

'Fate is kind after all . . .'

I remember listening with a detached air, but I said nothing. I knew they were being kind and caring but I would not let them influence me. I was on the brink of making a great change in my life. I was not yet sure which way to go but it would have to be my decision.

3

I was now ready to think positively about the future. I needed a job and I needed a home. I needed to be independent. In spite of family pressure, I would not consider a post in my father's school. Instead I would advertise.

To my surprise my advertisement in the *Church Times* – 'Young, qualified teacher seeks a teaching post with accommodation for herself and two young daughters, aged 3 years and 1 year,' brought many replies from private schools.

Why then was I drawn to an advertisement which appeared in *The Western Mail?*

'Required urgently, a County Supply Teacher for Breconshire.'

Such a post would mean travelling from school to school. My own transport would be essential. There would be no prospect of a home for me and the children in such a situation. Why then did I feel an overwhelming conviction that this was the job for me?

I dismissed the idea as being completely impractical and continued to sift through the replies, some enclosing an attractive prospectus in pleasant locations.

Then a month later, there it was again! The supply post for Breconshire re-advertised. This time I could not dismiss the compulsive force within me. I was not being led by the hand but felt literally pushed to apply for this post. It seemed as if my fate were being decided for me. My parents saw no future in what seemed to them to be a rash decision, but as usual they gave me their full support.

It was the first week of the New Year and a reply to my application came by return inviting me to attend for an interview on the following Monday. If accepted I would be expected to take up my new appointment on the Tuesday, the beginning of a new term.

The Director of Education was a large, wide, balding man in a brown tweed suit, a cream shirt and a brown tie. He smiled broadly with his mouth, but his brown eyes were unsmiling as he welcomed me. Having dealt with my application form, in a strong guttural North Wales accent, he explained, 'This is an unusual assignment, Mrs Thomas. You will be required to take over a small school for a year pending the appointment of a new headteacher.'

My heart leaped! A whole year!

'The village is Gwenddwr, near Erwood. At present, it is a Voluntary Primary School with forty-five children aged between five and fourteen years. There are complications, and so meantime all we are asking you to do is carry on your duties until the school is taken over by the Education Authority. Recently there have been several supply teachers, but the school needs stability for the coming year. I should point out to you that it is not going to be without its problems,' he said, anxiously glancing at my slight figure, 5ft 1 inches high. 'However, I understand from the testimonial which accompanied your application form that you are eager to find a home for your two children. There is a school house and if you have a successful year, you would then be able to apply for the headship. Are you interested?'

I stared at him in amazement. I could not believe what I was hearing. Then feeling very emotional I stammered a tearful, 'Oh yes, please!' He stood up indicating that the interview was over and shaking my hand he said kindly, 'Good Luck, *merch i* (my dear). We'll be here if you need us.'

Deliriously I descended the wide stairs in the Education Office. I was walking on air and musing light-heartedly.

Gwenddwr – *gwen* can mean smile and *dŵr* means water. Could it be a good omen? – smiling water! Could *Gwenddwr* be my *Minnehaha*?

Excitedly I told Dada my news. He had been waiting anxiously in the car outside the Education Office. He hadn't been at all happy that I was applying for a supply job. Secretly I think he was hoping I would not be successful and that he would be taking me home to re-consider my future. However, now the situation had changed, he said with a smile 'It could well have been a good move after all.'

'We'll take the Builth Road. We go to a village called Gwenddwr about fourteen miles from here.'

As we drove out of Brecon he said little, concentrating on his driving. He was not at ease in his new A30 and I knew he was missing the old Ford 8, (TH 7155) which had been his proud possession for sixteen years.

There was one memorable occasion a few years ago when we'd persuaded him to buy a new car and we'd waved goodbye to TH 7155 with great ceremony. Twenty minutes later he brought her back. 'I couldn't do it, Jen,' he said to Mam. 'She's been a faithful friend to me and as I drove around Cuckoo Bend on the Black Mountain, I could almost hear that engine saying "Don't sell me", so I'll keep her for a few more years.' Just before Christmas, eight years later he reluctantly admitted that the time had come to let her go.

I looked at him affectionately. He had the reputation of being a strict village schoolmaster, but he was a real softie at times.

4

We followed the instructions given to me at the Council House. We were to turn first left after going through the village of Erwood and sure enough, there was the sign for Gwenddwr.

As soon as we left the main road, we began to climb. It was a narrow winding lane that seemed to burrow its way through the hillside, climbing higher and higher alongside a steep cliff, clothed in dense brushwood, into a wilderness where rabbits darted from the undergrowth in fright, and hostile sheep and wild ponies stared insolently at these intruders who dared to invade their private world.

A sharp corner at the crest of the hill brought us out to the open windy peaks of the Twmpath and to our right, we looked down at a magnificent panoramic view of the beautiful Wye valley. I was to discover that every season would bring to this enchanting spot its own peculiar beauty and every visit would reveal new found treasurers, but that very first time, I saw a wild moorland clothed in heather, bracken and gorse, tumbling down to a lush valley, where the wide river lay silver and still. On the other side, the clumps of woodland on the gently rounded Radnorshire hills and the patchwork of meadows edged with hedgerows, showed up sharply in the cold grey light of a January afternoon, and the grave mountains rising in the distance seemed to stretch up to touch the pale wintry sky.

The road edged its way along the top for quite a while and then near a copse of tall Scots Pine trees it turned sharply to the left and soon the desolate moorland was left behind. For a mile or more, high hedges and sharp bends concealed the landscape around us, but we were aware that to our right the high ground humped around the winding track, which dipped up and down as the road formed a cleft in the hillside.

Dada drove slowly and carefully, aware of the danger of oncoming vehicles. Suddenly a sharp bend brought us out to a clearing, and in the valley to my left, I caught my first glimpse of Gwenddwr.

'Let's stop here, Dada,' I said pointing to a small lay-by in front of a field gate. My first impression of the isolated village was of a group of grey stone buildings and whitewashed cottages nestling together in a shallow basin of soft rolling meadows.

In front of us, the land tumbled gently away into a deep narrow hollow, where trees clustered around the hidden stream that skirted the village. On the other side of the stream, the land rose steeply to the village road and on a higher level, huddled on the gentle slope, the village buildings formed a frame to the village church, standing strong and placid against the wintry sky. Below the church, a solemn graveyard sloped down to the grey stone school.

There was no sign of life on that January day, not even a dog or a cat. Indeed it seemed to me like a lonely, forgotten village and my heart sank as we went on our way, down the steep hill to the stone bridge and then doubling back in a hairpin course, following the river towards the village.

I was to stay with Mrs Staley at Chapel House and we followed the directions given to us – past the Unicorn Inn on our right, past the long, high wall that supported the school playground, turning right at the village square and proceeding to the second grey stone cottage on the hill.

These then were the events that brought me here. I glanced at the time, just nine o'clock. I had come to bed early, feeling choked and emotional when Dada left.

'Get up that wooden 'ill, gel, you look fair wore out.'

Already my new found friend was understanding my needs. She had sensed I was too distressed to be sociable. Leaving the children had been a devastating experience. Why had I made such a senseless decision?

I was drifting into a slumberous state when I heard heavy footsteps and a loud hammering on the front door, immediately below my window. The visitor's voice was loud and gruff. 'It do look like snow, Jinny.'

'Keep your voice down, Jones, you'll be waking the new

teacher.'

'Good God, gel, you said you baint 'avin no more of they, afta' that other miserable cooten.'

'Ah well, this one be a poor little biddy and she do need motherin'.'

'God 'elp 'er, them buggers will 'ave gobbled 'er up by playtime!'

Muzzily I remembered the Director's warning. I needed time to prepare.

'Please God, let there be snow!'

5

I awoke to hushed silence and tangy cold air and before I opened my eyes I knew my prayer had been answered. From outside, light from the dazzling snow penetrated the soft cream curtains draping the windows on either side of my bed and filling the bedroom with a bright white glow.

There was a tap at the door.

'A nice cup o'tea to warm you up, Mrs Thomas. There be deep snow, so there be none of them children there today.'

She was in and out like a flash and a few seconds later, in again with a steaming jug which she emptied into the washbasin.

'I've lit the fire in the big room. You'll be wantin' to find your bearings and this snow will give you time to get settled before them kids 'ave a chance to take over.'

I studied her in the morning light. A neat little figure in a large patterned cross-over pinny. Soft, springy, steel-grey hair framed her round, weathered little face and her sharp dark brown eyes twinkled as she spoke. She was giving me my first lesson in classroom organisation. Somehow, my education lecturer in college had never succeeded in getting it across in quite that forthright way!

It was a lovely cup of tea – thin, strong and hot, just as I liked it. I eyed the expanse of cold lino between me and the washstand. Whether to take my pyjamas off before I got up, or after, was the question. I had not been accustomed to central heating, but there had always been a warm bathroom and a hot tank. In this situation, a quick dash in the 'altogether', an all over wash and back again to snuggle into bra, pants and stockings under the blankets would be better, and this became my regular routine on wintry days.

Thank goodness I brought warm slacks and thick sweaters, I thought as I dressed hurriedly – not to wear in school in front of the children, of course! That would not do at all, if I were to create a sedate school ma'am image. Today, however, I could be myself and I suddenly felt amazingly light-hearted, as I looked forward to a busy and rewarding day.

As I opened the living room door, the bacon was sizzling appetisingly in the back kitchen and I realized I was hungry.

I stood at the window and looked out at a silent world. There was no house opposite but the shabby stone wall, probably all that remained of the building in by-gone days, had undergone a transformation during the night. Shawled in white it framed a background to the clumps of green ivy dabbed with thick white icing which tumbled down, and the tufts of long grass growing in the stone crevices stood up stiff-whiskered and tall.

The lane was deep in snow but since the cottage was on a slope my view to right and left was limited.

I turned to absorb the warm welcoming scene behind me. There was a lively fire burning in the jet black range and a big iron kettle steaming contentedly on the hob. Two dignified china dogs guarded the assortment of shiny brasses on the high mantleshelf and on the wall opposite a large, loud-ticking mahogany clock. The table was laid with willow-patterned china, set on a spotless white cloth; an untouched patterned pound block of Welsh butter in a blue dish; home-made jam and home-baked bread. On either side of the fireplace, two high-backed chairs on a multicoloured rag-rug completed the picture.

That same sparkling scene greeted me each morning; and yet not once did I hear her cleaning that room. It brought to mind the story of *The Elves and the Shoemaker*, so secretly, quietly and efficiently was it done.

In the weeks that followed, that warm friendly room became my early morning haven where I daily enjoyed a period of calm before the storm.

'Get that down you, gel and then we'll be off down to the school.'

I looked down at the plate of crispy bacon, shiny fried egg and golden *bara saim* placed before me and tucked into the best meal I'd enjoyed for ages.

23

Thankfully, I snuggled into my warm hooded coat and my fur-lined boots, and together Mrs Staley and I stepped out into a virgin world where every ridge, slope and shoulder was shawled in white. I looked around me with interest.

'Fred and Elsie mind the Post Office,' she said pointing to the grey stone house at a higher level on the right. 'They two baint been married long, but they be no chickens. Indeed they be long in the tooth to be startin' married life, I be thinking, but that be their business. Fred's a little squirt but he got a kind 'eart. She be twice 'is size and could eat 'im up for supper if she'd a mind to,' she chuckled.

I noticed that a trail of her tiny footsteps wound their way from her front door down the hill to the village square. No one else seemed to have braved the weather.

As we crunched our way through the crisp snow, she carried on a running commentary.

'Penry lives next door to me. 'E be our road-man and should be out by now, old lazy bones! I'll give 'im wot-for when I do sees 'im.

'Next to the chapel, opposite, that be our village shop open on Fridays only, but Ray the Stores in Erwood do bring fresh bread on Tuesdays and I takes in orders for the hill farms.'

She trotted along, hands deep in pockets and her little brown felt hat pulled down over her forehead. From my lofty 5ft 3inches in boots I felt quite tall, looking down at my 4ft 9 companion!

As we approached the square, I noticed a more imposing house at the end of the road to our right.

'Caradog Jones our County Councillor do live there,' she added. 'The folks 'ereabouts calls 'im C.D. When 'e's got a wise 'ed on him, I calls 'im Caractacus but sometimes 'e got some funny ideas. Then I calls 'im Crackpot – to 'is face mind! If you can't say wot you 'av to say to one's face, there be no point in opening your gob, I reckon! That be the way I thinks anyroad.'

Off the main road, a short path led to the school gates, and from one of the terraced cottages nearby, we were greeted by an elderly neighbour. Mrs Staley introduced me, adding, 'Len do odd jobs for us.' He shook my hand.

'Be glad to help any time, miss. Just you put your foot down from the start and don't be letting them devils drive you away.'

My heart sank – yet another warning!

'Don't you be lettin' that bit o' lip from Len put you off, Mrs Thomas. 'E may be a bit of a busy-body, but 'e do mean well,' she said, opening the school gate which led to a large, rough, unsurfaced playground, supported by a retaining stone wall which stretched along the main road, following the length of the school boundary.

As the main road dipped, so the height of the wall varied from three feet at the school gate to near six feet at the end near the Unicorn Inn.

The tall criss-crossed wire fence of the playground was this morning transformed to a frosty pattern of delight. I surveyed the snowscape before me – wild, lonely and strange. First the sudden drop to the village road and then beyond the road, tumbling down to the river below, a gentle slope of wide evergreen trees, spreading their branches like floating umbrellas topped with icing, with mounds of snow hiding the brambles that covered the undergrowth.

Beyond the stream, a narrow lane climbed steeply between high hedges to the road above the village, and at eye level ahead, and all around me, the hills rose in hushed silence sloping gently down to the fat meadows that encircled Gwenddwr.

The beautiful scene filled me with emotion and I was reluctant to enter the stark grey building behind me.

'Come on, gel, you'll be fair froze out if you don't come in to the warm.'

6

She opened the main door with a large key and as I stepped in to the outside porch, I sniffed the old familiar smell of sweaty gymshoes, chalk and the disinfectant which had been liberally used at the large sink and wooden draining board behind the door. Spotless scrubbed flagstones led to a kitchen and the door to my right opened to the main school room. My first impression was of a high gabled room with pitched whitewashed ceilings from which hung two highly polished brass lamps. On either side of the room were two pairs of wide latticed windows set high in magnolia coloured walls – a classroom built at a time when it was thought desirable to confine children's attention to what was put on desks or written on blackboard, and prevent the excitement of the outside world from intruding into what was taught and learned in school.

However, I was relieved to observe that at the far end, on both sides, two large low windows with wide sills had been added, at some later date. The window to the left overlooked the school house yard, the high wall and sloping garden and from the window on the right, one had an expansive eye-level view of the rising hills and meadows.

I welcomed the warmth created by the roaring fire in the old black stove, which shone with inky black-lead, its belching pipe reflecting the glow from the outside snow. To the right of the stove stood an old-fashioned, high teacher's desk and as I sat on the chair, the china ink pot wobbled a welcome in its groove.

From my high position I surveyed my new domain. In spite of its antiquity every part of that lofty room was lovingly cared for – the scrubbed well-trodden floors, the brushed walls, the sparkling windows and the high beams. Not a cobweb or a speck of dust had escaped the caretaker's notice.

Facing me were twelve double desks in four rows with three desks in each row. Though gnarled and marked with initials, the

26

rich mellow oak shone with pride waiting for the desks' occupants. At the back was a wide service hatch which no doubt opened to the kitchen on the other side, and on either side of the hatch, two large double fronted cupboards, which seemed to be the only items for storage, apart from the unit of low open shelves behind my desk.

Cups rattled and up went the hatch revealing a small kitchen on the other side.

'A hot cup of Camp before you get cracking, Mrs Thomas. That'll warm the cockles of yer 'eart.'

I took it from her and saw the high shelves laden with gleaming saucepans and other cooking utensils, and the lower shelves stacked with china and trays of cutlery. To the right a calor gas stove and a calor gas fridge, her pride and joy. It was a compact and well-fitted area with a place for everything and everything in its place.

I was to find that Jinny Staley was a perfectionist in every undertaking and the excellence of her school meals was well known.

'Now, Mrs Thomas, you be staying in the big room today. No use nosing in the little 'uns room when there be no fire. Anyrod you got plenty to do to sort yourself out in 'ere. There be sandwiches and a flask of hot tea for your lunch. I'll be off now, I got the church to see to.'

The school door shut behind her with a loud clang and the muffled shuffling footsteps faded as she walked away, leaving me feeling desolate and alone. Outside the landscape now looked cold and grey. All was quiet except for the loud ticking of the old school clock.

Suddenly the whole situation seemed unreal. I trembled in panic. What was I doing here? Why did I leave home? How was Mam coping with two little ones bewildered by my absence? I had tried to explain to Sharon, but she was only three and little Lynne was still in her pram. I missed them so!

With my elbows on that high desk and my hands supporting my head, I gave vent to my emotions and had a good cry.

7

After that first emotional outburst, I realized that I really had to stop feeling sorry for myself and begin to think positively. There were a hundred and one things to see to, but with the school likely to be closed for several days, it would give me the opportunity to get myself organised.

The registers in the teacher's desk would give me details of the children on roll. The individual lockers would locate each pupil, and the exercise books in their desks would give me a general idea of the range in ability.

The book marked Requisition Orders indicated that no orders had been submitted during the current financial year, so that would give me a full year's capitation allowance to spend before the end of March. Hopefully the two large stock cupboards would reveal the existing supply of stationery, books and equipment.

First to the registers! There were forty-five children on roll with ages varying from five to fourteen years. Apart from the three children who lived in the village, the rest came from outlying farms where it seemed that many of the pupils came from the same family. Until the age of eight years the children remained in the demountable, partly-glazed building in the playground which served as the infants' classroom. At the age of eight they moved to the main classroom where they remained until they were fourteen.

The thought of being solely responsible for the academic achievement of every pupil from eight to fourteen, in every subject, irrespective of his or her individual stage of ability, was a frightening one.

I would need to be highly organised from the start. Alongside blackboard lessons, it would be worth my while to build up sets of colour-coded, follow-up work cards systematically and carefully, catering to the needs of every pupil according to the different stages of ability. These work cards would not only be a means of re-enforcing any lesson given, but also ensure that all ability groups were fully and purposefully employed; thus giving me the opportunity to give individual attention to those with problems.

Would it work, I wondered? Even in an orderly and well-disciplined group it would be a challenge, but from what I was gleaning from different sources, just getting the class to settle down to any kind of work was going to be a frustrating struggle.

Was I being over-ambitious? Suppose I couldn't cope? I couldn't face another failure! For months the break-up of my marriage had destroyed my confidence, but now I had the will to succeed.

I was in deep thought when Mrs Staley puffed in.

'Elsie the Post Office have had a message from the Brecon office,' she uttered breathlessly. 'They be wanting you to 'phone them. You dress up warm now! It be sharpish cold out there, cold enough to freeze a brass monkey.'

I should have notified them of the closure, I thought, as they put me through to the Chief Education Officer's office.

'Hello, Mrs Thomas,' he bellowed. 'I hear conditions are pretty bad up there. I'm ringing to let you know that we've arranged for a student teacher to join you as soon as it's possible. Her name is Janet Roberts, and hopefully she'll be with you until she goes to college in a year's time. Good luck! Don't hesitate to contact the office if you need advice!'

As I left the kiosk old Len came out of his cottage carrying a large shovel. 'I'll just be clearin' a path down the playground?'

He was being helpful and I didn't have the heart to tell him that I would rather crunch through the untouched snow, as the soft powdery flakes blew into my face and covered all existing footprints.

I sat down to tea and cheese sandwiches at the canteen counter and gave Mrs Staley my news. 'Where will she stay?' I asked.

'Don't you be botherin' your 'ead about that. I'll just be off to ask Elsie next door. She'll be sure to 'ave 'er. Anyway if she be near, it would be 'andy for you two to get together in the evenings to talk school.'

Off she went leaving me to mull over the situation. I had not expected a qualified teacher but had hoped, as was often the case in a country area, that an uncertificated teacher with years of experience would be available.

As things were, this young student and I would have to tread the same ground, as neither of us would have any experience in teaching infants. Therefore, as Mrs Staley wisely observed, we would need every opportunity 'to talk school', and outline a learning programme for the little ones, but 'slow and sure' would have to be our motto.

The stock cupboard to my right had four deep shelves bulging with books, most of them dating back to the year dot with faded and frayed covers. It seemed to me that no books had ever been discarded, as there were text books piled in sets, suited to the era when there were far more pupils. In fact the Log Book later revealed that at one time there were eighty pupils in the one classroom with just the one headteacher in charge!

On the top shelf sets of thin, ancient atlases; *History of the Commonwealth; Highroads into Literature, Tales of Other Lands*, all these pushed to the back and obviously not touched for years. But at the front, a treasure trove of the books I had loved as a child, well worn and faded in appearance but obviously enjoyed. There were thin individual copies of *Grimm's Fairy Stories* in grey covers, tattered and torn in places but carefully mended by those who valued them; a nature series of *Out with Romany*, bringing back so many memories of my own childhood; a set of *Collins Green Classics* including *Tom Brown's Schooldays, The Water Babies* and *A Christmas Carol* and many more old favourites – *The Princess and the Goblin, The Princess and Curdie; Anne of Green Gables; The Secret Garden* and *The Girl of the Limberlost*.

It would be my delight to introduce my pupils to these childhood favourites, too fragile to be handled, but I could make use of them at story time. I was so enthralled that I had only got as far as the top shelf when Mrs Staley arrived.

'Come on now, you've been and done enough for today. There be always tomorrow.'

Yes, very true, but the long evening and night lay ahead!

30

8

Throughout the day I was able to suppress all emotional feelings, but now with the day's work over, that sinking feeling inside me was already taking over.

Sitting alone in the cosy living room in the soft glow of the oil lamps, I found the ticking clock on the wall was a constant reminder of bedtimes at home. The children clean and rosy in their pyjamas, Dada in the armchair smoking his pipe; Lynne on Mam's lap looking cherubic with big blue eyes and soft golden curls. Sharon blonde and wiry, standing on a chair doing her usual bedtime routine going through her repertoire of nursery rhymes and demanding an audience.

'You, now, Nanna and Dadcu – sing "Baa-baa Black Sheep!" So the rich baritone voice and the clear soprano would blend in melodious duet. Both my parents were well known soloists in concerts, operas, oratorios, eisteddfodau and, of course, in chapel.

My brother Daniel and I were brought up in a house full of music and the walls of the school house reverberated with the voices of children practising, and the friends who regularly joined in a musical soirée on winter evenings. We were far more likely to be lulled to sleep by a rollicking quartet chorus from Gilbert and Sullivan and other harmonious classical renderings than a lullaby.

Life was never dull, but as we got older we weren't too happy when on occasions a musical gathering disrupted a planned family outing. A trip across the Black Mountain to First House pictures in Brynamman was always exciting. Dressed all ready, long before time, we sat with our legs dangling over the playground wall, dreading that the sound of the approaching car would bring unexpected visitors and knowing they would never be turned away.

'We'll miss "Rin-Tin-Tin" if they come today.'

31

'If I turn the clock on, we can leave before anyone comes.'

'You wouldn't dare!'

'I would! I'm fed up with visitors on Saturdays!'

Then there were Sunday evenings, when the sopranos, tenors and baritones sang in the gallery practising for the *Gymanfa*, the annual singing festival. Tap, tap went the baton as Dada, in the pulpit, demanded perfection. In a downstairs pew we sat anxiously watching the clock.

'At this rate, we'll never be home in time for *The Count of Monte Cristo.*'

Then there were Sundays when the anthem went really well, but what then? Supper over, table cleared and we would wait with bated breath. Our hearts sank when Dada brought out the anthem – not again!

'I'm still not satisfied with page three, Jennie. We're not getting it right!'

A big sigh from me and a big sigh from Daniel! It was going to be another long session. 'Goodbye *Count of Monte Cristo*,' we'd sigh and, cheesed off, we'd leave them to it.

I smiled now, remembering those occasions.

Dada would often quote, 'If music be the food of love, play on,' but it was the heroes of screen and radio that brought variation and excitement to our little world in those days.

I had always idolised my parents. I felt such pride in their vitality and their popularity. They supported every good cause and were very active in the war effort, but now my father was looking forward to retirement. Looking after Sharon and Lynne would be an added responsibility which they could well do without. I must do all I can to ease their burden, I thought, but outside the snow was falling in thick flakes.

9

During the week the snow continued to fall and the village street was rapidly filling in with drifts several feet deep. I awoke to hear Mrs Staley shout. 'Get that path shovelled from my door to the school gates, Penry. Mrs Thomas do need to get down to the school.'

Penry did as he was bid without saying a word. In fact, I don't think I ever heard him speak. He was a short, square, shy little man under a flat cap who always looked down when I passed by. So every morning that week I'd set forth into a vast white lumpy landscape hushed in silence, following my nose along a narrow sloping path hemmed in by walls of snow.

I kept to the same routine and worked like a Trojan every day. I explored every nook and cranny, gradually beginning to assess the needs of the school and the needs of the children who would be in my care.

A short time in the infants' classroom established that apart from a set of empty open shelves, there was no other form of storage and all existing stock was kept in the main classroom. The large stock cupboards revealed a set of *Beacon Graded Readers, Common Sense English* and green *Fundamental Arithmetic* books, which I had used when I was a pupil in the primary school; all were in reasonable condition and could be used for the time being.

A large cardboard box contained a supply of knitting wools and huge wooden knitting needles, large bundles of yellow, red and blue raffia with cardboard circles and rings in assorted sizes; squares of hessian with cross stitch patterns; a tin of mucky grey balls of plasticine which I quickly discarded because of likely threadworms.

On the top shelves I found tins of powdered paints in assorted colours; large sheets of white kitchen paper, grey sugar

33

paper and, thankfully, a supply of manilla cards which I would need to make charts and work cards.

Having established the supply of stock I was now in a position to review the situation. On the positive side, the school was well equipped with stationery and art materials but sadly lacking in pre-reading activities and assorted apparatus for number work and practical mathematics. I would need to give priority also to acquiring supplementary *Beacon Readers*; illustrated story books; nature and topic reference books; modern atlases; constructive and educational toys, wall maps and other visual aids.

Eagerly I planned the re-stocking. Shabby cardboard boxes could be replaced with brightly coloured containers and storage trays with the apparatus readily available when needed.

Not having to spend money on items of stationery and art materials would mean that I could be extravagant in ordering all the items I required, and the sooner the better. I came across a thick Arnold catalogue and assorted up-to-date book catalogues and by the end of the week the official orders were ready to be posted and marked 'urgent'.

The exercise books in the individual lockers indicated the wide range of ability within my class. It was obvious that the chronological age of each pupil had little to do with levels of ability. At different ages there were average pupils needing to be pushed, brighter pupils needing to be stretched and others, young and old, with obvious learning difficulties who would need individual attention.

I remembered the warnings and knew it would be to my advantage to get familiar with the names of each pupil *in situ* in preparation for D-day.

So with a set of long, white, card labels and black felt pen, I moved from locker to locker writing down the name of each occupant in large print. I placed them clearly visible on top of each desk to enable me to mark, learn and inwardly digest as I sat at the teacher's table examining the work in each exercise book.

In spite of all my preparations, I acknowledged that the challenging task ahead could be insurmountable and felt as nervous as on that first day when I started teaching at Eastville Junior School in Bristol.

Within the first month at Bristol I had blotted my copy book. It had been a good lesson. The class had enjoyed the story of Grace Darling and I anticipated exciting follow-up activities in free writing and art work. In groups, the children were eager to re-enact the story. First we had to create the dramatic atmosphere. Pencils tapping on the desk depicting the pelting rain; voices making the oooo-ing noises of the howling wind, the whooshing waves and at the front, the tossing lifeboat in the raging sea. Suddenly, there was a loud bellow from the doorway and Mr Bartholomew, the headmaster, stood there with a red face and eyes bulging behind his double lensed glasses.

'Go to my room!' he shouted at me. 'Mrs Toombs will take over your class.'

There was a deathly hush in the classroom as I followed him like a lamb to the slaughter. Ranting and raving, he did not give me a chance to explain. 'No control! no control! I'll not have any of that nonsense in my school. Don't assume that you can bring any of your modern ideas in here, young lady! Mrs Toombs will show you how to keep your class in order.'

Valiantly, trying to control my tears, I returned to my classroom. The Bibles were out and in absolute silence, the children were copying the 21st Psalm.

'A little trick that always works!' whispered Mrs Toombs.

Remembering that traumatic experience, I suddenly felt light-hearted. I was now being given the opportunity to create a meaningful learning situation in a stimulating and lively environment, as my education lecturer had encouraged us to do. No more would there be a tyrant like old Bartholomew making my life a misery.

Still, I'd better keep those Bibles handy, just in case!

10

Friday arrived and I had to accept that I wouldn't see the children at the weekend. On my way to school I stopped at the kiosk near the school gate and rang the Post Office in the village back home.

'Hello, Morgan Davey. This is Mair ringing from Gwenddwr. Will you tell my family that I can't get home. Have you seen anyone?'

'Yes, your Dad trudged through the snow to collect some goods yesterday. He went out carrying that teddy bear left over from Christmas. They are fine. Don't worry now!'

I left the kiosk feeling much happier and crunched my way towards school. The playground sparkled with bright beady crystals of untouched snow except for the criss-cross tracks of isolated birds who braved the cold.

As usual Jinny had been down early and the main classroom was warm and welcoming. I stood with my back to the foreground and let the warmth from the stove seep through my clothes.

I smiled at the thought of Dada and the teddy. I remembered that after Christmas, Sharon had gazed at the large teddy perched on the wide shelf behind the Quaker Oats. 'Poor teddy, isn't it sad that no one wanted him for Christmas. He hasn't got anyone to love him.' I had no doubt that she had since used the same technique on Dada and he had succumbed.

I remembered another Christmas Eve at the vicarage in Cyfarthfa. My cousin Mary's children brought in a stray kitten. 'Please can we keep him?'

'No!', said their reverend father who was preparing his Christmas sermon.

'But Daddy, it's a dear little kitten with no home on Christmas Eve and his name is Jesus!'

I decided I would make full use of the weekend ahead to

make the classroom lively, busy and attractive, so that is what I set out to do. My education lecturer in college, prior to teaching practice, used to say, 'Before planning your classroom displays, stand back and ask yourself: how can I use my displays to further the children's learning experience?'

Standing with my back to the canteen partition, I surveyed my classroom. The children would be facing four main display areas – two wide walls on either side of the fireplace and two substantial corner areas near the two large windows, where the sills could be used for further display.

I had brought with me an assortment of colourful Child Education pictures and for the area on the left I chose a large winter scene of children playing in the snow. Mounted on black paper and surrounded with labels on strips of white card, it brought that part to life. All labelling needed to be carefully planned, not only to be informative and challenging but so the daily contact with phrases and questions would help to extend the children's vocabulary and further their reading experience.

The wide window sill to the left could serve as a nature table and the wall display in the corner was ideal for brightly illustrated charts of winter birds, hibernating animals and in the centre a nature chart.

The book shelves behind my desk and the window sill to the right served as a display for reading books and library corner, and above a series of word-building charts. An attractive 'hundred' chart using bright colours to accentuate the 'fives' and 'tens' would lead to useful number games involving addition, subtraction and multiplication for the whole class. The answer was to tread slowly until I knew their needs.

Other wall areas to the sides and above the canteen partition would be ideal for topic work and the children's paintings mounted and labelled; those areas would develop in time.

If next week the pupils began to drift back to school I would be prepared. There was still much to do but it was a good beginning and I was pleased with the week's work.

Another day over and another evening to face. As I locked the door on that late Friday afternoon, the air was still and quiet and under grey skies the landscape appeared dismal and cold. I walked along feeling dejected and lonely. During the day keeping busy and planning ahead kept me in buoyant mood, but my spare time for brooding brought moods of depression. What was I doing here? I should be at home with my children. I looked up and saw the long zig-zag ribbons of smoke drifting up from the chimneys. Mrs Staley would have a glowing fire waiting to welcome me and the table laid for tea. I could not have chosen a more comforting dwelling place in my time of sorrow. With her lively mind and bright-as-a-penny personality, she always managed to shake me out of my dark moods.

'Mrs Thomas bach, you are lookin' tired biddy – indeed you are! Try this spot of brandy. It will perk you up no end. I do always keep a bottle of Martell 'andy – just as medicine mind!'

It was after tea she told me that I had been summoned to meet the Councillor, Caradog Jones, at six o'clock. "E won't be keepin' you long 'cos 'e do always listen to the Archers.'

She looked at me approvingly when I appeared wearing a grey skirt and a pale blue polo neck jumper.

'You play your cards right, gel. Who do know? That school house would make a right good 'ome for you and your little ones.'

It was a clear, crisp night and pale fluffy clouds scurried across the sky hiding a wintry moon. With the aid of a torch, I followed the cleared paths which led to the large white house on the square.

As I approached the front door, a dog barked from within and before I had a chance to knock, the door opened and he stood there in the glow of the lamp light. Mr Caradog Jones, Breconshire County Alderman and Chairman of Builth Rural Council.

He was short, a rotund little man in a rough brown tweed suit, a matching waistcoat and a collarless striped flannel shirt. His blue eyes twinkled in his round ruddy pink face as he greeted me and took my coat.

There was a strong smell of woodsmoke and the room spread into dark corners. Misshapen logs crackled in the big black iron grate and the yellow and red flames threw leaping shadows on the black and white collie lying near the hearth. In the corner, in a rocking chair, sat a large, grey-haired lady with a shawl around her shoulders.

He turned off the crackling brown wireless and pointed me to a chair near the large table covered with a yellow and brown oilcloth. Sitting on the other side, he studied me with his head to one side and his chin resting on his chest.

'Well, well,' he chortled with amusement. 'Them kids will have a field day – sure to, sure to! What do you say missis?' – turning to his wife. She smiled, nodding her head.

'Of course being it's a Church School, I have no say. I see teachers coming and going and that's how it will be until the school is handed over to the Education Authority. The vicar and I don't see eye to eye on most things but there's one thing for sure: we both want to see a headmaster appointed and living in the school house.'

My heart sank! Why did I come here?

A movement from the left startled me.

They came out of the oven, two large cats – one ginger and the other a fluffy grey. They jumped on to the table near me and quickly and nervously I moved my chair away.

'Don't mind them,' said Mrs Jones who spoke for the first time. 'It do take them time to take to strangers.'

Ignoring the interruption, Councillor Jones rambled on about the long-standing disagreement between the Church and the Education Department and the several issues that had to be settled. He emptied his pipe, rummaged in his pocket for his tobacco pouch and continued to talk with some authority, but I was finding it difficult to concentrate. I was too aware of the ginger cat only an arm's length away and at eye level, swinging her tail and staring at me with menacing green eyes.

I felt threatened, and avoiding the creature's scrutiny I let my gaze wander around the room. The lustre jugs and the brass candlesticks on the huge oak dresser gleamed in the rays of the red glass oil lamp. On the fern-patterned wall paper, darkened with resin, two large family portraits, in heavy frames, hung above the oak settle. With relief I saw that the hands of the grandfather clock indicated that it was time to leave. He glanced at the watch in his waistcoat pocket and fetched my coat.

'They're a wild bunch and I won't reckon you'll stick it for long – like the others. But all the best, lass!'

With my heart in my boots I said goodbye.

I wasn't ready to face Mrs Staley's cheerful chatter. Anyway, she was an Archers' fan too.

The sky had cleared and the cold pale yellow moon was peeping through the disappearing clouds. Buttoning up my fur-lined hood, I made my way in the moonlight down the village road alongside the high playground stone wall and towards the Unicorn. A bright light shone in the inn and as I approached from the bar came a hub of gravelly voices and raucous laughter.

I crunched past, not wanting to meet anyone, along the snow-wrapped road midst a vast white wilderness of patchwork meadows all edged with hedges of spiky twigs and white feathered hawthorn bushes. Soft powdery snow fell from the trees like dredged flour.

The moonlit landscape seemed unreal, strange and lonely, in tune with the sinking feeling inside me. I rested at the stone bridge, leaning against the wall and looking back along the river bank towards the village.

Common sense had told me from the start that I was far too young and inexperienced to be considered for a headship, but deep down I kept on thinking that there must have been some reason why, against all odds, I had chosen to come to this village.

I had always accepted God as part of my chapel upbringing. I had never questioned, neither had I given serious thought to what I really believed, but during the past three months I had received spiritual strength from some source. I believed that I had been consumed by a driving force which had brought me here for a purpose and I had the will to succeed. Suppose in my vulnerable state of mind, I had imagined it all and made a dreadful mistake! I shivered in panic. I had no choice but to carry on.

The moon was full and shining on the snow. In the river below, the dark water glistened in the moonlight. The whole countryside gleamed magically and I stood there on the bridge, a lone figure feeling wretched and scared of the challenge ahead.

11

On the Monday evening Janet Roberts arrived – a slender girl with gentle brown eyes and a shy smile. We had time for a short conversation only, as she needed to settle in at the Post Office with Fred and Elsie.

'There'll be none of them big boys there today,' said Mrs Staley on Tuesday morning. 'They be kept 'ome on the farm to go searchin' and diggin' for lost sheep.'

I breathed a sigh of relief. I needed the opportunity to work with Miss Roberts in the infant classroom. It was a large, pleasant demountable building, glazed on two sides from two feet off the floor to the ceiling. In such a raised position, the large glazed areas gave magnificent views of the school house garden to the right and the cottages beyond the garden wall. To the left was an expansive green meadow which extended to the grey cottages on the road beyond the school gate.

It was furnished with ten double infant tables and twenty small round infant chairs, a teacher's desk and an ancient piano that needed tuning. The black stove and fireguard completed the picture.

Apart from the long open shelves along the back wall there was no other cupboard for storage and all the stock needed to be carried from the main classroom. Gradually in twos and threes the children appeared, all eager to help. Before discarding caps and coats, we formed a crocodile, carrying pencils, crayons, assorted paper, counters, blocks and books from the main school. Unfortunately this meant crossing a few yards of playground. By this time everything around us was drip, drip, dripping. The hard snow slowly slid off the school roof and the down-rain pipes silenced for many days by glowing icicles, gushed out, overflowing the drains.

Boys and girls slushed their way through and their boots picked up lumps of frozen snow which melted in little pools on the classroom floor.

By playtime, shelves were stacked, a number frieze and alphabet frieze and a few Enid Blyton nature pictures decorated the two walls, the children were settled at their tables and the classroom was beginning to look orderly and 'lived-in'.

Mrs Staley arrived with a tray of steaming mugs. 'I did bring you all 'ot cocoa to warm the cockles of your little 'earts,' with her face wreathed in smiles. She stood there in the middle of the classroom in her cross-over pinny and her little brown hat pulled down over her grey curls. 'It be real good to see you all again.' The children beamed with pleasure.

She turned to us. 'Over there,' pointing to the front desk to the right, 'you got Marjorie and Gillian. They be Ray and Barbara's girls. Ray be our village blacksmith and the smithy is down that little lane that leads up to the Fron Farm. They do live in that cottage next door to Len, our 'andy man.

'Behind them, that's Brian. 'e do live with 'is granny Maud in Church House. That be the pink cottage over there beyond the school house garden. They be the only children from the village. The rest come from the farms. Margaret, David and Elved from Abergwenddwr. They be C.D.'s grandchildren.' I made a mental note of that information!

'Brynmor and Haydn be from Cefngarth, the farm near the stone bridge and Carol and Margaret come from the Fron Farm, the farm on the 'ill.

'David and Gerwyn be the boys who do come the furthest from Gellirhydd and the little one with big brown eyes be Irene from the Gurnos.

'These be the good ones, so make the most of the next few days before them rascals turn up,' she whispered to us as she bustled out.

I looked at Janet and laughed. 'That's telling us, so we'd better get cracking!'

Indeed, since most of the children present would be with Miss Roberts, I took the opportunity to work with her in the infants' classroom during the rest of the week. Meeting the pupils in stages in this way would help considerably. It gave us the time to assess the different stages of ability within her class, to plan a scheme of work which would meet their needs and to get to know them individually.

There had to be time for fun too. Outside play was out of the question in the wet, slushy snow, so action stories and singing games helped everyone to relax. The warmth from the stove seemed to have improved the old piano and it became a really honky-tonk session.

From that very first day, the school dinners were absolutely super, served with all the trimmings. What she didn't happen to have in the canteen, Jinny would bring down from home, or a bit of parsley from Len, a little sage from Elsie the Post Office or fresh mint from Barbara's garden. I noticed that those little items were never charged, because from the start she made it clear that I would be responsible for orders and bills.

'I did say when I did take this job. I do do the cookin', but I don't do no paper work; no orders and no accounts. That be the way it 'as to be, I reckon.'

Perhaps it was just as well. At least I could ensure that all the extra items which she contributed were included. I therefore had a great deal to do with Ray the Stores and Harold the Butcher – Ray the grocer, a jolly, chubby fellow in his late forties and Harold the butcher, tall with fair curly hair. 'He's so shy he wouldn't say boo to a goose,' she said.

Everything had to be top quality and on the rare occasions when Mrs Staley was not pleased, she did not mince her words. I was working at my desk in the main classroom. From behind the partition came,

'Mrs Thomas do expect the best and if she don't get it she be down on you like a ton of bricks.'

Poor Harold the butcher! I bet he quaked in his boots. I chuckled, knowing it was her way of keeping me on my toes, too, because that is exactly how she would expect me to react so she was sending me the message loud and clear. I had a great deal to learn, but I was to find that I had a good tutor, who would keep me on the right track! Old Len came down on our first day to clear paths to the WCs. She called them WCs but in reality it was a zinc shanty on the playground, divided into two sections by a zinc partition for 'BOYS' and 'GIRLS'. In each section there were two wooden seats with two holes in each seat and buckets underneath.

Even so, she took as much pride in making them presentable as she did everywhere else. The wooden seats and floors were scrubbed clean in each section and there was a liberal dose of pine disinfectant. I found that she made a daily inspection, and God help any boys who tried to aim over the zinc partition into the girls privy. She knew their tricks and that partition told its own tales!

Old Len's job was to empty the buckets, bury the soil in the school house garden and cover the earth with lime. I found that Len wasn't on the pay-roll either.

'I looks after 'im and gives 'im a few bob on Fridays.'

'Mrs Staley,' I said, 'do you have any wages left?'

12

Friday arrived and as soon as school was over Mrs Staley bustled in. 'Get your skates on, gel! I 'ave spoke to Ray in the shop and 'e do say you can have a lift to Erwood.'

I hurried off to collect my small case, already packed and bought sweets and chocolate at the shop before he locked the door. I knew he usually kept open until very late on Friday. He was looking rather harassed and I couldn't help wondering whether he had been bullied to give me a lift.

I sat in the front with my case on my lap. A mixture of familiar smells wafted from the boxes and baskets filled with fresh bread, vegetables, fats and sides of bacon. He obviously brought fresh produce on Fridays because I had noticed that the shop was well stocked with assorted tins, soaps and cigarettes.

Off we went, bouncing over lumps of hard snow and splashing through slushy pools created by the thaw. Even so, we bypassed deep and solid snow drifts not likely to disappear for some time. The late afternoon sky looked flat and cold and the trees and hedges along the winding lane looked black and bare without their snowy drapes.

Soon, we were out on the open moorland spaces of the Twmpath into a grey desolate landscape. A small group of mountain ponies, with manes hung low, huddled together beneath a clump of pine trees. Here and there sodden sheep searched for patches of green, and bleated miserably.

I was grateful for the lift. Squelching along on foot in this isolated 'lost world' would not have been a pleasant experience. I was excited because at last I was going home to the children.

'Is that a buzzard?' I asked when a large bird with a wide wingspan and speckled feathers swooped down low, ahead of us. He didn't really want to talk.

'Yes, you'll be seeing a lot of them flying low when the rabbits get lively and when it's lambing time.'

45

The bird rose gracefully and I watched it wheeling and falling over the bracken. He drove slowly down the steep winding slope and soon we were out on the main road.

'I'll walk from here, thank you very much Mr Williams.' I walked briskly across the bridge and the stiff cold wind whipped cold blasts into my face. Walking a long distance in this would have been unbearable.

I realized that this would be a path I would have to face in all weathers during the coming year. How else would I go home at weekends? My plans for coming and going were very uncertain. The rail journey from Erwood via Llangammarch, Llandovery, Llanwrda and finally to Llangadog was fairly straightforward. Dada would meet the train and take me home, but returning to Gwenddwr on Sunday, when there were no buses and no trains, was going to be a problem. A weekly journey by car over the Sugarloaf Mountain to Llanwrtyd and then through Builth Wells to Gwenddwr would be too much for Dada, especially since he needed to be back in time for chapel.

Waiting on the empty platform for the train, I realized that I had been rather selfish and inconsiderate not to have given serious thought to this dilemma. The other route via Brecon was just as long, but Janet's parents had offered transport from Brecon to Gwenddwr late on Sunday evening. How to get to Brecon was the problem.

From far off I heard the whistle of the train. Soon the signal went down and the train came steaming in. I humped my case into an empty compartment. The whistle blew, the door slammed and I was on my way home.

Home again to innumerable pleasures and the comfort of the old school house. Huge hugs from Mam; shouts of excited laughter and chatter from the children as they wrap their little arms around my skirt and legs. Dada standing by, his eyes glistening with tearful emotion.

In our living room a roaring fire burned in the ornate marble fireplace, and the leaping red and yellow flames casting a warm glow on the red leather bound furniture. A welcoming scene! It was so good to be home.

In the firelight, we relaxed on the red sofa, Sharon chattering

46

incessantly and Lynne competing, with her own baby talk. My gaze wandered to the high glass-fronted bookcase, now in shadow but filled with the books I would always treasure as being a permanent part of home. Its contents were imprinted on my mind, so often had I lovingly dusted and re-arranged them – the complete set of Scott's novels bound in red and gold; Dickens, a row of dark blue; the stories and poems of Thomas Hardy; the complete works of Shakespeare; D.H. Lawrence, George Eliot and Chaucer's *Canterbury Tales*. Then on the lower shelves, copies of Welsh literary novels, the *Mabinogi* and the family Bible.

There was another closed cupboard below, bulging with manuscripts; a collection of music; copies of choral works, oratorios, folk songs; music for sopranos, baritones, duets and quartets – all telling the story of my parents' love of music.

Appetizing aromas wafted from the kitchen, indicating that supper would soon be ready, but first the fun of bathtime, the usual repertoire of nursery rhymes and a bedtime story. My time at home was short and on these weekends I needed to savour every precious moment.

My parents would be eager for news, and with the children in bed, now was the time to tell them all about my fortnight in Gwenddwr. Was it only two weeks? It had seemed much much longer.

Laughing, we sat down around the kitchen table to have our meal. My portrayal of events and of the village folk, especially Mrs Staley, had caused great amusement but I did not tell them of my visit to Caradog Jones. After all, they were not convinced that I had made a wise decision to go to Gwenddwr, and I was not yet ready to admit that they could have been right!

Mam's meals were always creative and tasty, making the most of herbs and other interesting ingredients. Tonight, we were having roast wild rabbit with savoury stuffing and redcurrant jelly. Tomorrow, no doubt there would be rabbit stew, using the leg joints with diced carrots, turnips, onions and sage. Whether it be rabbit, chicken or boiled bacon, she always managed to create two meals from each bird or animal.

A trip to Llansteffan to dig for cockles was great fun and

afterwards home to suppers of steaming hot cockles, in shells, piled on soup plates with a knob of butter; the rest, set aside for the following day. This time, shelled cockles served in a creamy chive sauce – our favourite.

Of course the generosity of the local farmers greatly contributed to our weekly fare. My parents freely gave their services to the community, organising lively social activities in music and dramas. Saturdays were spent in training and preparing the pupils for concerts, eisteddfodau and operettas. Then Sundays after chapel, it was time for choir practice.

In return, the farm folk showed their appreciation and came bearing gifts of milk, eggs, butter, buttermilk, a pigeon, a rabbit or a chicken. At pig-killing time, which varied from farm to farm, came baskets of pork goodies – pork joints, spare ribs, port fillets, home-made brawn and faggots. When the salmon came up river to spawn, our secret visitor proudly presented his offering – but not a word to a soul! And there was no finer meal than Mam's fresh salmon cutlets.

So we always ate well and rationing during the war had little effect on our diet. In fact Mr Wilkes, the evacuee teacher from London who came to live with us, said he'd never eaten better.

Poor Mr Wilkes! Daniel and I hadn't taken kindly to him initially. We had been looking forward with excitement to having two evacuees – two boys or two girls to be in our spare bedroom. To our disgust, when we gathered in the school room to welcome them, it was suggested that we took the teacher.

He was a very nice man – good-looking too, but we were prejudiced. There came a Saturday when we decided he was a spy. After all, a bomb had dropped on the railway at Brynaman, on the other side of the Black Mountain. Pieces of gravestones flew everywhere! It was aimed at the storage tanker on the siding. There had to be a spy because no one, just no one, would drop a bomb in a little place like Brynaman unless there was a secret reason – so we thought.

I was practising the piano in the study the following Saturday, when Daniel came in looking very mysterious. From under his jumper he brought out a newspaper found in Mr Wilkes's waste paper basket – *The Daily Worker*.

'Just look at this anti-British propaganda,' he whispered. We huddled on the settee reading the headlines.

'It's like Lord Haw Haw', I said, looking shocked.

Off we went, looking for Dada. He was in the living room in his Home Guard uniform and reading *The Western Mail*. We stood in front of him, with solemn faces.

'Dada, Mr Wilkes is a spy,' Daniel said.

When Dada is taken by surprise, he doesn't say 'Eh?' quickly, but 'Eh-h-h-h?', taking a long time, and looking at us in astonishment over his glasses perched on the end of his nose.

We showed him the *Daily Worker* and waited for his reaction. His nose began to twitch as it always did when he was trying not to laugh.

'No! No! Mr Wilkes is not a spy. He is a communist.'

'What is a communist?'

'Well, they have very strong ideas about the way everyone should be governed; just like the Russians!'

'Is Timoshenko a communist?' asked Daniel who had named our corgi dog after the brave Russian general.

'Yes, I'm sure he is,' said Dada 'and he is on our side, just like Mr Wilkes, so no more talk of spies, please!

Later I told Daniel that when Uncle Jack came back from America talking politics, Grandad Garnant had said, 'Our Jack is talking like a communist.'

'When I saw him,' said Daniel, 'I thought he looked like an American gangster.'

I must admit, I too thought he looked like James Cagney in his navy pinstripe suit and slouch hat.

Lying in bed that first night, those childhood memories came flooding back. They had been happy days! I had been so obsessed in blocking out the unhappy memories of the past four years, and in so doing, had been reluctant to allow myself to dwell on former happy times.

Perhaps now I was beginning to recover.

13

Next morning I awoke to bounces and giggles. They were tickled pink to find me snuggled in between. When I came to bed I had carried Lynne from her cot to our bed where Sharon lay asleep. I know I was setting a precedent, but this was a time when we all needed special treats and being able to cuddle up to them was a great comfort to me.

'Look, Mami.' They chuckled with joy waving pyjamaed legs, bouncing and showing off their clowning tricks, Lynne endeavouring to copy Sharon's every move.

'Tell us a story, Mami.' 'Li'l B'ack Sambo, pese,' said Lynne.

I began, 'Once upon at time . . . and the first tiger said . . .'

'No! No!' said Sharon. 'You say, "Show me how the tiger looked",' – so I did!

They crawled on the bed, gnashing teeth and growling.

'. . . and the tiger said,' I continued.

'No! No!' said Sharon. 'You say, "What did the tiger say?" ' – so I did!

'I'm going to eat you up,' they both chorused.

It took a long time to finish the story and it was late morning by the time we were washed, dressed and ready to go downstairs to have breakfast.

Ben the postman was there having his usual morning cuppa. As far back as I remember, Ben had been our postman – more than a village postman, really, because in a scattered rural area such as ours, where there were many isolated farms, Ben was more like a social worker, always concerned for the welfare of others and always there to help in an emergency.

I particularly remember one memorable occasion. I had been ill for several months with rheumatic fever, and once up and about, the recuperation period was long and never-ending for me.

'Let me take her for a ride in my side car,' said Ben to Mam.

50

At that time postmen had motor bikes with a red mail box at the side.

I looked at Mam with my heart in my eyes. She knew I longed to go. She hesitated, 'I don't know what Dada would say.'

I prayed she wouldn't ask, because he was only next door in school, and I knew he'd say 'No', because I was still too weak to walk.

'Ah well, it's a lovely morning! If she's dressed up warm, it will do her good.' Ben carried me out in my thick red coat and red woolly cap to the red mail box and sat me on the mail bags.

'She's well camouflaged in that get-up,' he said.

'Ah yes, but they'll wonder why the lid is up,' said Mam, laughing.

Soon we were zooming along the country lanes, past luscious green hedgerows decked with yellow primroses, columbines and above, fluffy pussy willows and dangling 'lambs' tails'. Into farmyards we went, where sheepdogs rushed out, barking excitedly and farmers' wives greeted me with surprise and pleasure.

'Bought you a special delivery today,' said Ben.

It was a wonderful childhood experience never to be forgotten. I had been weak and ill for so long, but that day in the spring sunshine, the countryside was alive in all its glory and it felt so good to be part of such a wonderful world.

I reminded him of that special day, so long ago.

He was obviously a favourite with Sharon and Lynne too and they made a fuss of him. He was eager to hear my news. He would remember those days when I had looked eagerly for the letter that never came.

'Getting to Brecon on Sundays will be my problem,' I said. 'I have been offered a lift from there.'

He puffed at his pipe. 'Let me think. Didn't I hear that Twm bach the bus has had the contract to take a busload of Polish immigrants over the mountain to the pictures in Brecon every Sunday evening? I'll have a word with him!'

I gasped! I knew about the Polish immigrants who had settled in a colony a few miles away in Llanddeusant, but the bus

51

depot was in our village. I knew Tomos would be glad to give me a lift, because he used to drive our school bus to Llandovery Grammar and I got on well with him when I was the 'bus prefect' years ago.

Indeed Ben called back later and it was all settled.

'Well, I never,' said Mam and I once again experienced that uncanny feeling that things were going 'my way' for a purpose.

14

Monday morning! We had arrived back late on Sunday night. The roads were now clear but still banked by mounds of frozen snow.

'They'll all be 'ere today,' said Mrs Staley.

I'd get down early, I thought, but not early enough! As I opened the school gate, I saw a group of hefty lads gathered outside the privies. They slouched, hands in pockets, dressed in below-the-knee corduroy trousers, collarless flannel shirts and flat caps worn at a rakish angle. They talked and laughed loudly and their voices carried:

'Well, 'ere she be!'

'She be a trim little filly, baint she?'

'We'll soon deal with this nipper!'

Then as I got nearer, 'Mornin' Miss,' with wide cheeky grins.

During the next days, weeks, yes even months, these six lads were going to be the bane of my life, so I'll not introduce them by their real names but as Aled, Ianto, Shoni, Tomi, Guto and Wil, all with weather-beaten faces, bright eyes and solid frames. Not tall for their twelve to fourteen years, but taller than my 5ft 1 inches!

My well laid plans for a smooth takeover were in disarray by playtime. Initially when they were seated in their desks they were surprised when I already addressed them by name, but by playtime the older boys had got wise to my method and accordingly changed over seats when they came in from the playground. The first day was a nightmare!

'Don't be takin' no notice of them,' said Mrs Staley who was on the other side of the partition. 'The more they do see it do worry you, the worser they do get.'

They took every opportunity to disrupt class lessons by being generally unruly, falling about laughing at any misdemeanour by any one of the six and flouting all my attempts at discipline. It was just as well that I had prepared colour-coded readers and work cards which enabled me to work with the rest of the class individually, because class lessons were impossible. Any attempts at dealing with any one of the six, at my table, or at their desk, brought forth banging of lids, stamping of feet and wolf whistles from the others.

As the days and weeks went by, I had to admit I was making little headway. I had been so anxious to create a first impression by controlling the discipline from the start, but the more red-faced and harassed I became, the more they took advantage of my inability to cope and control.

In bed at night, I'd lie awake with my head throbbing. The whole situation was worse than I had expected. I had believed that if I were well organised and my lessons well prepared, the rest of the class would settle down to a daily routine, but we were up against a background of noise and disruption from the gang, who did very little work and who were continually attention seeking.

I felt devastated! I had always believed that teaching should be lively and stimulating. What was I doing now? Was my teaching lively? – No! Was my approach stimulating? – No! What had happened to my sense of fun? Why was I always standing in front of them looking po-faced and dictatorial? Teaching was no longer a pleasure for me and I was making that very obvious.

What was my education lecturer's favourite quote? 'If children are given a reason for learning, they become eager to know the mechanics of learning.' How then was I to set about it?

Already I was very aware that at thirteen and fourteen the older boys were just biding their time until the end of the school year. They were bored. School to them was completely divorced from the realities of every day life. Their only interest apart from planning devilry was farming. It came across loud and clear, not only in the playground when they talked in a group, but if a farmer passed by leading a bull to the cow, they'd run to the fence shouting raucous encouragement.

It wasn't only at break time either, because from the classroom they had a good view of the meadow across the river.

'Hey, look at that old tup,' shouted Ianto.

I was hearing a child read and looked up with interest. 'What's a tup?'

'Hey, boys, she don't know what a tup be!'

'It be a ram, miss.'

They clustered around the window in great mirth.

"E be late, baint 'e? I bet 'e did stray when they was tupping.'

"E be after them sheep now, any rod.'

"E be a dead loss at humping. Get on with it ye old slow coach.'

'E be too late for 'is own funeral 'e be.'

If I had been in control, I'd like to have followed that little bit of excitement with questions about 'tups' and 'tupping' and 'humping', but they already took great delight in embarrassing me at every turn, and occasionally without giving due thought, I gave them the opportunity.

'Have you any balls?' I asked rummaging in the P.E. box.

Back came, 'I got two', 'I got two', 'I got two', 'I got two' and they fell about laughing.

I couldn't help wishing I had the courage to say 'Good! All I need now is a good strong bat,' but I just buried my head in the box and pretended I didn't hear.

However it got me thinking. For my own sake as well as theirs I needed to change course. If I were to introduce a 'Farming Diary' it would give them the opportunity to discuss and write about the events of the farming year. I would need to rely on the older boys and girls for information and this could give them a sense of importance and responsibility. If I showed them that I accepted I had a great deal to learn from them, they might be more ready to accept me as a willing learner.

I would need to think it out very carefully, of course, but it might be the answer. The sooner I began to link some of my lessons to situations in their own environment, the better. If I made a concerted effort to make their learning programme more varied, more meaningful, hopefully it would make a school day more enjoyable for them and for me. Soon it would be spring and a good time to introduce farming news and link their writing activities to nature and life on the farm.

15

February had arrived full of flat white skies, dark bare trees, cold feet, chilblains and red noses. It was too cold for outdoor playtimes so morning and afternoon breaks were discontinued and instead we often had an extended dinner time.

Mrs Staley contrived to create a warm feeling of contentment in all those who partook of her delicious meals: roast beef served with roast potatoes and puffed up Yorkshire pudding; roast pork with stuffing and apple sauce; lamb, always with home-made mint sauce; nourishing stews with dumplings. These courses were followed by light, light steamed puddings with custard, or yellow creamy rice. These are just examples of the school menu. They were always happy family occasions and I noticed that there were never any discipline problems during meal times.

That fact should have been telling me something, shouldn't it? However, I was still too pre-occupied with their other antics. The old saying goes, 'The devil finds work for idle hands', and during those indoor playtimes every day brought some new form of devilment.

The boys had realised that I was very nervous of the old sow that always managed to get into the playground. We had no way of keeping her out, short of asking for her to be removed from the field next to us. She always managed to find a hole in the hedge. This large, ambling creature would come snorting and shuffling towards me whenever I ventured out.

'Shoo! Go away!' I'd shout as I went to the privy, which was around the back of the school house, but making a pretence at chasing her away, they'd always manage to cause Lizzie to dart wildly in my direction. She was always hovering outside the porch door and I later found that they rewarded her with tit-bits. So when the porch door and classroom door were left open, in she'd come, causing a great commotion.

Ianto was the one who could ride the beast, whilst the others chased her around the desks to yells of delight from the rest of the class.

From day to day I never knew what to expect. Life was never dull. Having determined to relax, I was trying to show a sense of humour and caused more amusement when I dramatically sought refuge in the high chair at the teacher's high desk, which was never used at any other time. Here was an opportunity to have something exciting to write about and indeed the afternoon produced promising free writing, crayoning, and clay models of Lizzie.

I felt quite chuffed! I had managed to turn a difficult situation to my advantage and next morning when, with expression, I read out their compositions and pinned up their crayoned pictures, they responded with glee. Laughing with them, I said to myself, 'I believe we are beginning to communicate.'

The large boxes containing the first of the requisition orders began to arrive. After playtime in the afternoon, the infants joined us in the big room and each large parcel was opened with great ceremony. Two at a time, the older ones took turn at unwrapping the brown paper and the rest of us looked on with 'Oohs' and 'Aahs' as the contents were revealed. Out came a selection of brightly illustrated story books; boxes of coloured beads in assorted sizes; pegs and peg boards; counters; brightly coloured construction toys and interlocking blocks. There were sets of dinky cars in different colours; table games, snakes and ladders, ludo and draughts. All these caused great excitement and I realised that the best was to come.

I had ordered a box of model farm animals which I had kept aside until last. Instinctively, I grasped the opportunity for a game which would involve them all, especially younger pupils.

The different animals were presented in different containers, and Shoni and Wil held them up for all to behold and called out in strident voices as if in an auction:

'Ten sheep; five cows; two horses; eight hens, one cockerel, six ducks, two dogs.'

On the blackboard I chalked a pictorial record and I set them off with the first few questions, circling each group of animals.

'Which is the biggest group? Which is the smallest group? Are there more ducks or are there more hens? How many more? Ten sheep, how many legs? Five cows, how many ears?

They took turns making up their own questions. Everyone joined in the spirit of the game. I sat back, thinking. The farm was teeming with mathematical situations. From an early age, even before they came to school, they were counting pigs, cows, sheep; or eggs collected from nests in the hedgerows – all invaluable learning experience. They met new mathematical experiences with confidence because it was part of living on the farm. Yet they struggled unsuccessfully in school. Would they not react far better if the exercises in number, measuring, capacity, weight and money were related to the mathematical experiences that they faced on the farm? Capacity could be linked with milk yield. Weight – feeding the animals; weight of fodder; potato picking and weight of sacks; the weight of wool. The cost of milk, eggs, butter, potatoes – market prices, and mart prices for sale of animals, would give us profit and loss. And I could well teach time by times of day, the farmer's calendar.

All this rich material offered tremendous potential for a meaningful syllabus in mathematics, covering every aspect of number and practical work from the infant stage to leaving school.

It would take time to prepare graded work cards and activities at different stages but if, in so doing, they were given a reason for learning, it might make them realise that it was worth coming to school after all.

16

I wish I could say that my reawakening and my determination to unwind, to be less tense, brought a change in the classroom. There were times I believed we were beginning to communicate, but with the continuing dismal weather which prevented outdoor playtimes, they gave vent to their high spirits indoors. I accepted it would be a long process.

I continued to plan positively and long after the children had gone home, I would carry on working on new schemes of work in language, free writing and mathematics which related to the children's own experiences and environment.

In the dusk of a winter's afternoon, Jinny would light the oil lamps, bustle about the classroom, sprinkling used tea leaves on the classroom floor. She'd jabber about this and that and I'd carry on working. However, one afternoon, she appeared with a barrel under her arm, one of those rounded cider barrels.

'Just look what I did find in the corner of the boys' privy! Them be real devils!'

I wasn't surprised. I'd noticed their flushed faces. 'Are you all right?' I'd asked, as in turn they kept asking to be 'excused'.

'Sick, miss,' came the reply; 'Bellyache, miss,' as they shuffled out one by one.

It could be the prunes and custard, I thought. At least they were quiet, and I welcomed the silence, to work with the younger ones. It was not until home time that I began to suspect that there was mischief afoot. They were decidedly sleepy.

I'd better check in case they are ill, I thought, but when I stood in front of them, I knew. They weren't ill. The rascals were drunk! The comings and goings meant that they had been drinking since dinner time. What now? If I ranted and raved, it would have no effect. In this intoxicated state they would defy me. What would be the point of making an issue of their insobriety if I couldn't deal with it effectively? Far better to deal with them tomorrow, so I let them go and said nothing.

However, long after they had gone, when I was done, I sat at my desk resting my head wearily on my hands. There were days like this when it seemed I couldn't carry on. If it became common knowledge that the older boys had been drinking in school, it would be obvious to everyone that I was not able to control them, just like the other supply teachers who had come and gone.

I could not afford to fail. It affected me psychologically and left me feeling hopeless and helpless. It was obvious that this was a delayed reaction to the trauma of being rejected. I could feel all my self-confidence draining out of me at the very thought of failing again.

From outside came the jovial chatter of men's voices obviously in high spirits after market day. I looked at the school clock – six o'clock. The once-a-week bus had arrived. The sound of shuffling footsteps on the gravelly school playground, and then the clanging of the main door, heralded a visitor.

In came a hollow-chested figure in a long black overcoat and a bowler hat. The glow of the hanging lamps shone on his chalked, wrinkled face and the damp strands of white hair hung like cotton grass from under the bowler hat, perched precariously on the top of his head.

He waved his stick and staggered towards me, shouting aggressively, 'I be Jones your school governor,' in a slurred voice.

Yes, I'd already guessed who he was, having been warned that this was a character to be reckoned with – forthright and fierce! Even the vicar was said to be nervous of him. How should I handle him? He was obviously more than slightly sozzled. I remained sitting at my high teacher's desk. It would be to my advantage to be at eye-level because on ground level he would tower over me. He leaned on his stick and glared at me across the desk, with his glassy pale blue eyes.

'Ye be too soft with them big lads, techa. It be the stick they do need! You got to rule them with a hard rod!'

Had he heard about today, already? I put out my hand to greet him. He was swaying unsteadily. I came down from the high chair.

'I know what you need, Mr Jones, a nice cup of tea. Then you can tell me all about it, and I will tell you how you can help me.' I led him to a chair in front of the fire. 'Mrs Staley says, "It be Jones the Cwm who will help you".'

He came willingly and was obviously surprised at my reaction. I went into the canteen and put the kettle on the gas stove. I raised the hatch, feeling safer behind the partition.

'I am not surprised that you are angry, Mr Jones.'

'Well, there be no sense in it,' he shouted loudly. 'She be left stranded! When she did get back to her car they was all flat. An' she in a swelter to get to a woman in labour. Devils they be! Devils!'

So it wasn't the cider! Obviously he was referring to the District Nurse and the boys' antics after school.

I made the tea and took in a cup for him and a cup for me, and sat in a front desk facing him.

This was news to me. I hadn't heard about Nurse Morfudd.

'I am so very sorry. I, too, am very worried about their behaviour. They are doing their best to drive me away and I could really do with your support as my school governor. I know that they respect you and they are afraid of you too.' I smiled appealingly. 'Will you do me a favour, Mr Jones? Will you come up to morning service tomorrow and come down on them like a ton of bricks? It would help me greatly. I have no one else to turn to.'

The tea had mellowed him. He gave me a wan smile.

'Don't fret, lass! I'll soon deal with them buggers!'

Our first meeting, which could have been confrontational had ended well and he was to become a good friend.

Ten years later, when I was being interviewed for the headship of Yorkswood School, I was asked, 'This will be a Birmingham Council Estate and you are likely to have to deal with aggressive parents. Do you think you will be able to cope?'

So I told them about Jones the Cwm on market day and added, 'I believe in welcoming aggressive visitors into a friendly environment, firstly to calm them and then deal with their problem.'

'Did you say calm or charm, Mrs Winfield?' asked the Chairman.

I smiled. 'A little of both,' I said, and got the job!

17

I think I can safely say that this is when the tide began to turn. Mr Jones kept to his word and arrived at ten o'clock which gave me enough time beforehand to have our morning service and used as my theme, 'Thank you God for the people who help us'.

We sang the hymn:

> Hands to work and feet to run
> God's good gifts to me and you
> Hands and feet he gave to us
> To help each other the whole day through.

'Let's thank God for the people who help us,' and the children gave their contributions:

'Thank you God for our father who works hard on the farm,

Thank you God for our mother who looks after us.

Thank you God for Mrs Staley who cleans the school and cooks lovely dinners.

Thank you God for Mr Len who helps Mrs Staley empty the WC buckets.'

In turn came the vicar, the teachers and eventually the one I had been waiting for – 'our nurse'.

'Tell me, how has the nurse helped you?'

'When I fell from a tree, miss.'

'When our father broke his leg, miss.'

'When our mother had her babies, miss.'

'Hands up all those whose mothers have been helped by the nurse when they were having their babies.'

A forest of hands went up.

'Suppose she had not been able to get there in time. What do you think could have happened?' I looked at their solemn faces. 'Yes, some of you might not be here today,' and I glared at the culprits.

'Well, Mr Jones the Cwm, our school governor came to see me last night and he was very angry. Four boys from our school were seen fooling about near the nurse's car which was parked in a gateway. Nurse Morfudd had left it there and walked across the fields to see a patient. She had been busy all day and still had more to do. A mother in Crickadarn had started labour pains and she was anxious to get to her, so she was hurrying. How do you think she felt when she got back to her car, feeling very tired, to find all the tyres flat?'

Ohh! I saw a sea of serious faces and four who were decidedly shame-faced. 'That is why Mr Jones the Cwm is coming here this morning.'

They looked startled. 'I'll say no more. We'll just sit quietly and wait.'

I looked at the clock – five to ten. I hoped he'd come soon! The waiting seemed endless. When he came, the knock on the classroom door was loud and the partition shook! In the grey morning light, he looked even older. He must be in his eighties, I thought!

The utter silence seemed to unnerve him. He stood in front of the class leaning on his stick and breathing heavily. In his deep, quivering voice he ranted about 'the boys who did not care; the boys who did not want to learn; the boys who were always behaving badly; the boys who would soon be leaving school but would not be of any use to anyone; the boys who brought shame to the school.'

As he became more emotional, he raised his voice, his words rising to the rafters. He rocked unsteadily and it was time I intervened.

'Mrs Staley will have a cup of tea waiting for you. Thank you very much for coming, Mr Jones. I am sure we all feel ashamed and we'll be writing to Nurse Morfudd to tell her that we are very sorry she has been treated so badly by boys in our school.'

It was a cold but dry day, fine enough for outdoor playtime. I asked Shoni, Ianto, Guto and Twm to stay behind. There was the incidence of the cider not yet dealt with. This was my opportunity to kill two birds with one stone, as they say. I brought in the offending barrel and placed it on the table.

'Your behaviour in school yesterday afternoon was bad enough but what you did after school was unbelievable. What do you think Mr Jones would have said if he knew that you had been drinking?'

From my desk I brought out the four envelopes addressed to their parents. 'I have no doubt that by the time your parents read this, they will have heard about the tyres but then they will realise why you behaved so foolishly. You must have known the problems it could have caused in the emergency and all the people in the community will condemn you. I cannot believe that you would have played such a stupid prank if you had been of sound mind.

'Since the beginning of term you have been wasting my time and wasting your own. You consider that you are too grown up to be in school but growing up means being responsible and being mature. Do you know what that means?'

'No, miss.'

'It means knowing how to behave and setting a good example to others. It means being in control of what you do, so that you do not cause a problem or danger to others. Do you really consider that your behaviour yesterday was being "responsible" and "mature"?'

'No miss; sorry miss! Won't do it again, miss.'

'After all, this time next year, you'll be expected to hold down a job, and being your last teacher, I could well be asked to give you a reference. At present I can't think of anything good I could say about you.'

I instinctively felt that this was an opportunity to be approached with caution. If handled wisely, I could be on the brink of solving the long term problem. So far I had failed to curb the boys' continual disruptive behaviour, but now the situation had changed. Here I was addressing four dispirited and dejected transgressors. Gone were the cheeky grins and the defiant expressions. A little compassion from me at this time might cement a new relationship. It was worth a try!

'Look lads, for the past weeks we've had a long battle, but whether you like it or not, I am determined to stay, and you still have five months to put up with me.

'Together we could make good use of that time to improve your skills so that you are better prepared to face the outside world in July. That means reading, writing and understanding.

'I have no doubt that you can cope with every day tasks on the farm, but farming is changing and you will be expected to do far more. Already there are government grants with all the information and regulations and if you don't know how to deal with them, you'll miss out. There will be new farming equipment with instructions to follow. There is talk of electricity coming into the area when each farm will be assessed according to the information being given.

'You will be able to meet these new challenges so much better if you have the learning skills to deal with them. As you receive pamphlets giving you information, bring them to school and we'll discuss them together. Then there are forms to be filled. You'll have a far better chance to have a job if you can show that you already have a knowledge of what is offered and understand what needs to be done. If we work together, I can help you and at the same time you can help me.'

They looked surprised.

'I know you find lessons boring, don't you?'

They looked embarrassed.

'Well, I want to make the work far more interesting, but I need your help. I want to link the work you do on the farm with the work we do in school but I'll need to "pick your brains" because you know far more about farming than I do.

'When we do "farming news", we'll be writing about the farmer's work and all the problems he faces throughout the year. In arithmetic we'll need to know about market prices; mart prices of farm produce; the gallons of milk you produce; the weight of the food you give to the animals; the sacks of potatoes.

'I'll be relying on you to bring in all this information. I am giving you this opportunity to work with me instead of against me. Is that too much to ask? Think about it carefully and at the end of the day I'll want to know what you have decided. Meantime, you stay in.'

I left them in the classroom and joined Mrs Staley for my coffee break. It had been a long 'playtime'.

65

For the rest of the day we worked in subdued silence. I made no attempt to give lessons but while the children carried on with set work, I dealt with each pupil individually, hearing them read, marking their work and checking individual, specific needs and difficulties. I chose to give helpful encouragement rather than criticism. It was a heaven-sent opportunity. Now that we were approaching half-term I needed to assess their overall attainment during the past weeks. This respite from disruptive behaviour was therefore a beneficial blessing.

At the end of the day, Shoni, Ianto, Guto and Twm came to apologise. 'We want to work with you, miss'.

'So, we are all going to make a new start are we?'

'Yes, miss.'

'Right, in that case, I'll tear up these letters.'

It had been a hard struggle but at least I could see a glimmer of light at the end of the tunnel.

18

The end of February brought brighter hours. Walking to school, I noticed the damp, re-awakened earth. The frost of January had helped to clear the ground leaving it clean and fresh. The bare, dark brown trees were a sharp contrast to the enriched grassy green meadows.

To the children's delight, one day I suggested a nature walk and after dinner we followed the winding lane over the river and past the blacksmith's forge. On every side there were thickets of birch and hazel but the cluster of catkins were no longer drab and grey but beginning to change to a golden brown. Here and there in the hedgerows, shy snowdrops were peeping through. We heard the rush of water in the stream, the bleat of sheep answering the call of a newly born lamb, and the haunting call of the curlew.

What did we expect to see in the winter sunshine?

They walked along in groups, their faces beaming with pleasure and chatting easily in unaffected local dialect.

'Look at that there drey, miss.'

We stopped to look at the round nest of twigs high up in the tree.

'Miss, see that shiny patch on the bark. That be where the squirrel runs down from the nest. See them scratch marks!'

They searched for the hidden store of nuts and acorns.

'See where it 'as stripped the bark.'

'I bet it be a grey. We don't see no red no more.'

Avoiding the main road we crossed a field to a coppice.

'We might see a hedgehog.'

'Not likely, miss, the sow, she be sleeping until March.'

'Once, miss, I did see a hedgehog climbing a stone wall.'

'Look, miss, here be a likely pile of leaves.'

'Last year I did find a nest of naked babies under a pile like that.'

We decided not to look in case we disturbed a nest of young babies.

They chatted animatedly in their natural surroundings. After a while we came out of the copse and surveyed the landscape, the expanse of the Twmpath covered in bronze bracken. The silver ribbon of the Wye was all a-glitter in the February sunshine and beyond, the lofty hills of Radnorshire marked the horizon.

Immediately in front of us, the slope was steep and covered with thick undergrowth of moss and heather. Joyfully the children ran slipping and sliding, screaming and laughing as they gathered speed, tumbling and somersaulting as they reached the bottom.

'Come on, miss!'

They were eyeing me with a challenging look, anticipating that I would gingerly pick my way over the uneven ground. However, on an impulse I decided to forget my role as headmistress. With gay abandon, wrapping my winter coat around me, I took the plunge. Off I went sliding and slithering through the heather, accompanied by shouts of encouragement, surprise and delight.

My backside was sore and scratched, and I must admit to a feeling of foolishness as I landed at their feet. I looked up and saw their beaming expressions. They gathered around me. I really think they are beginning to like me, I thought, and felt a great sense of satisfaction.

That night I lay in my soft bed with the hot water bottle at my feet and snuggled contentedly. My body ached after the afternoon's physical exertion but spiritually I was elated.

It had been an enjoyable and successful afternoon. As I listened to their unselfconscious chatter, I realised that they had a wealth of language. How different from the stilted language of their class work, being too conscious of their inability to speak and spell correctly and therefore reluctant to express themselves freely. I would need to use every opportunity to encourage free expression in talking and writing. Of course there needs to be guidance in correct speech and grammatically correct writing, and time must be given to spelling, but it must be done sensitively and meaningfully so that the pupils are encouraged to 'have a go' and feel confident in relating those learning skills to their own free expression.

As a young child who spoke only Welsh for nine years, I remember how very self-conscious I felt when I timidly attempted a few phrases in English. The set exercises taught in school had instilled the need to be grammatically correct at all times, but it was difficult to relate these grammar rules to what I wanted to say, so I was reluctant to try.

During teaching practice in college a tutor turned up in my lesson when the class was working through miscellaneous exercises in *Common Sense English*. She called me aside.

'Let me tell you a little story,' she said. 'When I was a young teacher, I was exasperated because Tommy in my class kept on saying "I have wrote" instead of "I have written", so I made him stay in during a games lesson to write "I have written" a hundred times. Half an hour later, he ran out waving his sheet of paper. " Please, miss, I have wrote, 'I have written' a hundred times. Can I come out to play now?" So do you understand what I am telling you?'

Yes, her message was coming across loud and clear, but there remains a school of thought that believes that every grammatical error in speech must be corrected immediately and every spelling mistake in a passage of free writing corrected. I was already finding that this had a devastating effect on free expression. That was another reason that I found myself in Old Bartholomew's bad books. He was one of those! He expected to see red lines through every bad spelling so when a not-so-bright little girl called Jane proudly showed him her gold star and my comment, 'This is a good try, Jane. Well done!', he took out his red pencil and mutilated her work with red lines and all my work in trying to build up her confidence was undone. However, he didn't always have his own way.

Hovering nearby, he heard Johnny bring exciting news. He stood in front of the class with shining eyes and proclaimed, 'Last night me dad caught a burglar!'

Mr Bartholomew corrected him. 'My dad caught a burglar,' and Johnny shouted exultantly, 'Oh, sir, did your dad catch a burglar too?'

69

I chuckled, remembering I had disappeared behind the blackboard to control my laughter and I left 'Sir' standing there looking red-faced and flabbergasted.

The candlelight flickered, throwing shadows around me. I had come to bed early but had whiled away the time thinking and reminiscing.

'Here I am, little room, sharing my thoughts with you but tonight there are no tears.'

Tomorrow I would be going home to Sharon and Lynne not for a short weekend but for eight whole days!

19

I arrived home on the Friday to find everyone busy preparing for the concert on Saturday, which always meant a hive of activity. Young farmers came to set up the stage and convert the classrooms into one main area. With partitions drawn back, the whole school building became a hall in the shape of a letter 'L', with the infants' room at the side of the stage being an ante-room for the performers.

Wives and young girls arrived on Saturday morning with baskets of food to prepare for the after-concert supper. On these occasions the school house was also used – the kitchen for preparation of food, the large living room for dining, the study, to receive the chairman and special guests and, if it were a drama or operetta, the bedrooms used as a dressing room. In fact, when it was a dramatic performance, I'd arrive home to find all our living-room furniture on the stage.

For some months I had hidden from the public gaze but now with renewed confidence, I was happy to mingle with everyone in the kitchen and in the school. All welcomed me with affectionate greetings, all eager to know how I was getting on.

Sharon and Lynne, too, were in their element, enjoying the attention and running around here, there and everywhere, looking like two little cherubs in their blue dungarees and white jumpers; skipping and bouncing on the wooden stage was a great experience and they chuckled with joy at the reverberating sound which filled the school hall.

All, young and old, were bubbling with high spirits, enjoying the opportunity for companionship and anticipating the evening's social event. After all, they were hard-working farming folk often living in isolated farms, so preparing for an event of this kind was a welcome chance, amid the hustle and bustle, to catch up with the latest gossip.

Tonight was to be a concert in aid of the Red Cross.

Musicians from my parents' circle of friends were often well known artistes, who were prepared to give their services free, so there was no difficulty in arranging a concert party and the standard was always high.

That evening, the children's bedtime was delayed, giving me the opportunity to make a brief appearance before the performance. The hall was full and buzzing with chatter. From behind the curtain I scanned the audience. They were the familiar faces that I had known throughout my growing-up years – grandparents, parents, children and grandchildren. All welcomed me with a wave, a nod and broad grins to show they were happy to see me.

Once the children were tucked up in bed and asleep, I decided to stay with them, concerned that the clapping, the whistles and stamping of feet and the shouts of 'Encore, Encore' would awake and frighten them.

I wrapped the eiderdown around me and in the glow of the Kelly lamp, I settled comfortably in an easy chair near the window. Just below to my left was the large rear window of the school hall, already steamed up and I could see the smudged shapes of the young men who always stood at the back.

There was always immediate silence when Dada appeared on the stage. All his ex-pupils knew that 'Mishtir' would have no hesitation in calling out the name of anyone who caused a disturbance.

'I wish Dada wouldn't do that,' I'd say to Mam. 'It's so embarrassing.' In fact, Daniel and I had acknowledged that there were disadvantages in being 'Mishtir's' children. Everyone expected us to be so good. Any mischief afoot, and we were excluded for that reason. Boys chased other girls, putting worms down their jumpers, but they never chased me!

After school, Daniel and I would wander down to Gellicaerau feeling miserable, knowing that we had not been included.

'It's not fair! I am tired of being called a "goody goody".'

'I would never tell on them, would you?'

'Never, ever!'

We sprawled amongst the buttercups, and the sheep just stared.

'Let's shut our eyes and think of something really wicked.'

'We could get some yellow chalk and write rude words on the school wall.'

'What shall we write?'

'Let's write 'DAMO JIAWL' in big letters. It's a real bad swear word.'

'We would have to own up, because others would get the blame.'

'Would you be brave enough to tell Dada?'

'No, I don't think so.'

'I know! Every time we are fed up, let's come down here and shout swear words and the Black Mountain will shout back.'

We stood there, side by side, facing the wide expanse of the lofty hills and green meadows and gave a great yell.

'DAMO JIAWL!'

And as the frightened sheep ran in all directions, the Mynydd Du echoed our cries. We rolled on the grass and laughed our heads off. It felt really good to be wicked. Gradually we built up quite a repertoire of swear words and on the way home we'd sing.

'They went to heaven and flip, flop they flied

Flip, Flop, they flied,

We went to the other place and friz, froz we fried

Friz, froz we FR-I-I-IED.'

I suppose nowadays it would be described as a therapeutic experience!

Indeed, these days, I was finding reminiscing a therapeutic remedy. It was my way of switching off from present troubles. I listened. The concert was obviously a great success. Every performance whether tenor, baritone, soprano, duet or quartet, was loudly applauded.

As always there was a request for Dada to sing 'The Sergeant Major on Parade' and for their duet 'Tell me gentle stranger' and 'Trot here and there'. Quietly I opened the window and Mam's dulcet soprano notes infiltrated the darkness.

'Lo, hear the gentle lark', was always a favourite. It was the song she sang in her first Welsh Rarebit broadcast. The newly discovered Harry Secombe was also on that programme.

Next day in the village shop, Mrs Morgan the Post Office had said, 'Fancy putting that comedian on with Madam Jennie!' Little did they know that one day he would be so renowned!

I well remember those radio broadcasts. We'd sit around the table in the soft lamplight playing dominoes or draughts, in front of a bright fire crackling, and the iron kettle hissing on the hob. There'd be butterflies in my tum, as with nervous excitement we'd watch the clock and wait for zero hour. Then came the thrilling moment when her lovely voice came over the air and her perfect rendering, whether it be from Handel's *Messiah*, from *Madam Butterfly* or just a simple Welsh folk song.

From the school hall came loud cheers, whistling and stamping, indicating that the concert was over.

Soon the artistes would be coming in for supper. Everything was already prepared, the dining table laid and a welcoming fire burning. As always there would be merry chatter, hearty laughter and an atmosphere of sheer enjoyment and satisfaction that always followed a successful event.

20

After a happy week's holiday, I returned to Gwenddwr to celebrate March 1st, St David's Day.

We filled the classroom walls with a daffodil frieze and the children's paintings of the Welsh dragon; and after our radio service on Dewi Sant we sang Welsh folk songs.

I was very aware that these children had no awareness of their Welsh heritage and no Welsh was spoken. The 1870 Act which had imposed an English educational system on all Welsh schools had had a devastating effect on this area. The Welsh language had been banned so that when a child was heard speaking Welsh, a flat board known as the 'Welsh Not' was placed around his neck. When that child heard another speaking Welsh, the board was passed on and the one wearing it at the end of the day was caned.

Surprisingly this 'Welsh Not' had been zealously used in Gwynfe school at the same time, but the language in the home had survived. Gwynfe had remained a strong cultural Welsh community, but in Gwenddwr the language had died.

Deiniol Williams, the Director of Eduction at the time, was anxious to re-introduce Welsh to our school curriculum and we received Welsh books and a Welsh comic called *Hwyl* which was to become of great interest to me, because many years later Ifor Owen, a renowned historian who created *Hwyl*, was to be my neighbour, and his wife Winnie became my dear friend.

My first aim was to make the children aware of their Welsh background and to give their village its beautiful Welsh name – Gwenddwr. Probably this was once 'Gwernddwr' which meant 'the water of the Alder tree', because alder trees grew all along the banks of the village stream. However to me, Gwenddwr would also have the special meaning of 'Smiling Water' and I was determined to encourage the children to pronounce the

Welsh name correctly, knowing full well that Elsie Bevan, the Post Office would continue to say,

'Who the bloody hell does she think she is? It always have been Gwenda and Gwenda it will be.'

It was all very well for the children to have tales of Alfred and the cakes and Bruce and the spider in their history books, but they needed to know that their home area had played an important part in Welsh history and I would introduce them to the wondrous tales of their Welsh heritage.

Did they not know that The Drovers' Trail passed this way? Flocks of sheep and herds of cattle were driven across the Epynt mountain on their way to the English markets in London. The drovers knew every path from Wales to England, keeping to the highest places to avoid the toll-gates and having to travel very slowly in all weathers to allow the animals to graze along the way.

Had they not heard that it was the region where Prince Llywelyn had fought against the English King Edward and won great victories in Brecon and Builth? It was near Builth, in the small village of Cilmeri that our last Prince of Wales, Llywelyn, who had led his people for twenty five years, was killed. The memorial stands there for all to see, but of course with one or two exceptions, there were no cars in Gwenddwr and apart from the bus to Builth, which was on a school day, the children never had the opportunity to travel out of the village.

Every part of the curriculum seemed to present a new challenge and there were not enough hours in a day to do everything.

True to their promise, the older boys were bringing in news from the farm, and we were into Class Farming News. During the preceding weeks, the ewes had been brought close to the farms in preparation for lambing. At night with a lantern, farmers went searching for wandering ewes who were ready to lamb. We'd heard of a newly born lamb found beside a dead ewe and carried into the kitchen, wrapped up in a sack and revived with warm milk. Pupils also reported the custom of fitting a dead lamb's woolly coat on to another orphaned lamb so that the ewe who had lost her lamb would recognize the scent and accept the orphan as her own. However, when no ewe was available, the children thrilled in rearing orphaned lambs, feeding them with a bottle, so that they became tame and behaved like pets.

Sows, too, had given birth and careful watch had to be kept, sometimes all night, lest they crushed their litter.

The old gander who often charged at me with outstretched neck and flapping wings when I passed by on Fridays, was now wandering around the farmyard looking forlorn. He was waiting patiently for his new family to emerge whilst the geese sat protecting their eggs and covering each egg with hay and down.

Those were items of news already entered in the Class Farming News. The children kept their own farming diaries, and errors in grammar, spellings and punctuation were set aside and dealt with in language lessons rather than discourage free writing sessions. As a result there was a more confident response from all age groups. Samples of their corrected work in neatest writing were then pasted into the Class Farming Diary with crayoned illustrations.

Yes, indeed, days passed smoothly, not without problems of course, but lessons were far more orderly and enjoyable and at last I felt I was in control. I would have to tread my new path with care – be resolute, be patient, be tolerant and above all be of good humour and have a sense of fun.

With new confidence, I was more optimistic. So when Mrs Staley suggested it was time to have a peep at the school house, I agreed.

The key to the front door hung on a nail inside the canteen. The school house formed the gable end of the main school building. The three stone steps leading to the front door lay immediately opposite the main school door.

Crossing the threshold that dinner time, I discovered that the ground floor consisted of three separate quarters, a spacious parlour, a good-sized living room and beyond, a lean-to scullery.

From the living room a steep staircase led up to a tiny landing with a small window that overlooked the Unicorn Inn; to the right a spacious beamed bedroom with a small gable window overlooked the front schoolyard and at eye level the meadows.

To the left was another beamed bedroom, which included a little side room above the stairs. In this bedroom the gable window overlooked the sloping school house garden and beyond the hedge, the solemn graveyard and the grey stone church surrounded by tall yew trees.

In the grey light of a March afternoon, the little house looked forlorn and neglected. I wandered from room to room getting the feel of the place, noticing the drab yellow ochre washed walls, and the brown paint on beams and doors which accentuated the atmosphere of gloom.

However, the house had limitless possibilities. In my mind's eye I visualised the walls upstairs and down, stripped of their dingy colour and adorned with fresh spring-like wall paper and the beams, doors, window frames and staircase painted in sparkling white.

As far as I could see there was no sign of damp or mildew. The gaps under the skirtings and the latched rickey doors would no doubt give access to draught and mice but with a little D.I.Y. that problem could soon be remedied.

All the rooms were quite spacious and downstairs the unusually large, small-paned windows, let in ample light. In the parlour, was a delightful small Victorian fireplace in dark red tile, set in a decorative iron-framed mantlepiece, painted white. In the living room, the black iron range was sadly in need of attention. Both fireplaces backed on to the main school room, probably sharing the same chimney; which explained the house's warm temperature.

I walked through to the scullery, empty except for the porcelain sink in the corner near a low, large window overlooking the paved yard. The long wall of the lean-to scullery was obviously an extension of the long, 6ft-high stone wall which also supported the sloping school house garden.

Beyond the high stone steps which led from the yard up to the garden was the privy. This little stone house, containing a wooden seat with a hole and a bucket underneath, had whitewashed walls, a scrubbed seat and bright lino. Jinny took great pride in its appearance and thankfully arranged for the bucket to be emptied regularly. However, it was quite a distance from the back door and would not be a pleasant trek in wet and wintry weather.

I stood at the bottom of the steep, creaky stairs and stared through to the parlour and back to the living room and the scullery beyond.

Could I really create a home for the children and myself in this sad little house? Given the opportunity, had I the courage and endurance to see it through? Suddenly the bright mid-day sun slanted through the windows and there was a welcoming glow as sunbeams peeped into dark corners. I had a strong feeling that here there could be a promising future, God willing.

21

'Look out! I did just drop my big knife! Any time now, there's sure to be somebody important coming over that Twmpath. So look out!'

This wasn't the first time that the partition had gone up to make this dramatic announcement and even though, at first, it had the desired effect of creating silence, I was beginning to think that Mrs Staley was 'crying wolf' too often. However, on that particular Wednesday in mid-March, it actually happened.

They were chanting their tables when he appeared at the door – a short, slight, balding man with a pale serious face and perched on the end of his nose a pair of gold rimmed *pince-nez* spectacles.

'Good morning! I am Leslie Richards, His Majesty's Inspector of Schools.'

My heart began to thump and my ears began to throb. The only time I'd ever seen a schools' inspector was in my father's school when I was only seven, but to this day I would always remember the consequences.

At that time, salaries were based on attendances and all registers had to be marked and closed by ten minutes past nine. On that day the total attendance had not been entered in the infant classroom because the teacher had allowed extra time for late arrivals, so her register was not closed when he arrived.

The result was catastrophic. All registers going back several years had to be sent to the Education Office in Carmarthen to be examined. For days there was an atmosphere of tension and anxiety when our dining table was cluttered because Dada insisted on re-checking every register. Mam and Dada worked on them far into the night. For me and for Daniel it was a traumatic experience. At home where there was usually singing everywhere – in the kitchen, in the bathroom, in the toilet – for those unforgettable days we lived in a house as silent as the grave.

My startled expression must have conveyed my immediate reaction.

'Just carry on as if I were not here, Mrs Thomas,' he said, wandering around the classroom.

I took a deep breath and counted to ten to calm myself. I no longer felt I was sitting on a time bomb because the older pupils were far more co-operative and supportive. My new learning programme was producing encouraging results and in arithmetic, whether dealing with numbers, money, or measuring, I was following a routine where at the beginning of every lesson I addressed the whole class irrespective of age or ability. Because I was very aware of the 'more able' and the 'less able' I dealt with their particular needs and could direct my questions accordingly. I felt that all pupils benefitted from lessons of this kind and no one was excluded. Colour-coded work cards at different stages involving exercises in addition, subtraction, multiplication and division ensured that they received plenty of follow-up practice in mechanical skills.

This week we were dealing with capacity. Information about the quantity of milk produced on each farm had been gathered and the results were neatly presented on the blackboard alongside the capacity table chart. Since this was a hill-farming area the milk yield was low and the calculations well within their capabilities in changing gallons to quarts, quarts into pints and pints into gallons, thus giving practice in applying the 2, 4 and 8 times tables.

However, as a blackboard lesson it was also a good exercise in comparisons and a good opportunity to get the children involved in a question and answer session. For the 'less able': which farm produces the most? How much more? How much less? For the 'more able': how many gallons produced in a week? in a month? They were responding with enthusiasm and I was well pleased.

Later when we were having coffee I explained to him why I had adopted this particular method in dealing with the wide range of ability which included some bright youngsters who needed to be stretched with the older pupils, and at the same time, cater to the needs of those of all ages who were slow learners.

'I am not here to do an inspection today,' he said, 'but it was suggested that I called to see how you were coping. You seem to be managing quite well, Mrs Thomas.'

I decided to be honest.

'Believe me, Mr Richards, if you had called a month ago, you wouldn't have thought so. It has been a hair-raising experience!'

He looked at me kindly over his glasses. 'Good luck, *merch i*, I know a little of your circumstances and I hope all goes well for you.' Then as he left, 'Next time I visit Gwenddwr to give a full inspection, I hope to find you still here.'

As soon as he had gone, up went the partition and Mrs Staley stood there with a wide grin and her eyes twinkling.

'That be another hurdle you've cleared, gel!'

The children bounced in after playtime and looked up at me expectantly.

'Yes, I am really pleased with the way you worked with me this morning, so this afternoon we'll go out looking for frog spawn.'

After a good morning's work and a fine lunch, off we went down to the stream, carrying jam jars along the zigzag path of the bank. Here and there at our feet, grew bright starry celandines and pale lemon clusters of fresh-faced primroses nestled in the hedgerows. Puffs of yellow pollen wafted from the dangling hazel catkins as the birds chirped and fluttered among the branches.

The blackbirds chased each other to and fro, seeking a safe area for nesting, and the birds that had already staked their territorial claim sang aggressively to warn away those that dared to invade their chosen boundary.

Along the bank of the stream, the smooth, shiny reddish brown bark of the young alder trees contrasted starkly with the tough black bark on the more established ones. Near the male catkins that hung from the branches, we found the small female catkins with red scales. Next year the seeds produced by the female flowers would fall into the water and float down the stream to disperse in other places.

This might not be the best place to look for frog spawn after all, I thought, but soon we came across a muddy patch where twigs and grass had formed a stagnant pool where the water had broken through on part of the bank.

'Over here, miss!' but we found not the slippery, black spotted jelly we had expected. Instead, hundreds of tadpoles with shiny black heads and wriggling tails, clung to the green weed. The boys dipped their hands and with palms cupped they shouted with glee as they trapped the tiny writhing creatures.

'Who needs jam jars,' they cried, plunging their cups into the pool, but the girls were well prepared with their jam jars and made sure that they collected plenty of pond weed.

We were back in school by playtime carrying bunches of catkins and the silvery pussy willows. Carefully we emptied the tadpoles and green weeds into a rectangular glass container we'd found in the cupboard and placed it on the nature sill.

'Did you notice the patches of slippery jelly still there at the edge of the pool? Where had the rest gone do you think?'

'Floated away, miss.'

'Gobbled by trout, miss.'

'Eaten by birds, miss.'

'Yes, that could well have happened, but when the black spotted eggs which were protected by the jelly began to change into tadpoles, they began to eat their way out of the jelly and when the head and tails were developed, they then fed on the pond weed. It will be up to us to look after them now and keep an eye on any changes.

'Soon back legs will appear and their tails will shorten and disappear. That is the time to ask Mrs Staley for a shallow bowl and we'll put large stones in the water to give them the chance to begin their lives on dry land, before we take them back to the river bank.'

On the board I wrote down the words they'd need for their nature diaries and they did their own crayoned illustrations.

'By the way, there is a long word for the change from egg to frog, but it's a very long word and I don't expect you to remember it.'

'What is it, miss?'

'Well the word is metamorphosis.'

I knew from past experience that children love to chant long words like Constantinople and true to form after school, as they skipped out to the playground, I could hear 'MET – AM – ORPH – OS -IS'.

It brought to mind Trevor who was in my junior class in Bristol – not one of my brighter pupils but he had shown particular interest in my natural science lessons.

'I loves them long words, miss,' he said as I marked his Nature Diary. 'I knows them all. Hibernation, migration, pollination, oxygen, carbon-dioxide, metamorphosis.'

'Ah, Trevor, but do you know what they all mean?' said I.

Walking back to his desk, he said loudly, 'Can I open the window miss, this stuffy room is full of metamorphosis?'

Ah well, you can't win them all.

22

A letter arrived from the diocesan inspector informing me that he would be visiting the school at the end of May for the school's annual diocesan inspection.

I scanned the syllabus – the list of stories from the Old Testament; the life of Jesus and Psalm 24 to be learned for choral speaking.

It was quite a challenge. No one had thought to warn me! I would need to use morning assembly and R.I. lessons for the New Testament and story times in the afternoon for the stories from the Old Testament. Linking them to drama and creative activities might make the task more enjoyable and hopefully more effective.

When I mentioned the visit to Mrs Staley, 'This is your chance, gel. Go all out for them Bishops' Certificates. If you can impress Lord Muck and Big John, you'll be half way there.'

I gathered that Lord Muck would be the diocesan inspector and even though I had not met him, Big John was her name for the vicar, who was over 6ft tall. With a trail of supply teachers coming and going, and not being there on Sundays, he probably didn't see the need to introduce himself. Bearing in mind my recent problems, perhaps it was just as well! On the other hand it is a wonder that he would not have heard of the nurse's predicament from Jones the Cwm.

Jinny had obviously anticipated that possibility. 'I did tell him "Jones – don't you be tellin' tales to the vicar about them boys in school or you'll be sayin' goodbye to them cups of tea every time you do call for bread." '

What would I do without her?

The days went by and slowly we were ploughing through the scripture syllabus, linking stories with drama whenever possible. The infants always joined us for morning assembly so the life of Jesus needed to be presented in as simple a way as possible.

It was about this time that I faced another predicament. Even though the older boys were no longer any serious problem, periodically there were isolated examples of disturbed behaviour which needed to be handled carefully. There was one sullen, moody boy very much a loner in the classroom and the playground. He made no effort in his work, took exception to any form of help and encouragement and often reacted aggressively to correction.

I must have a word with the nurse in case there's a problem at home, I thought.

Meanwhile, however, I couldn't let him get away with messy and unfinished work so rather than confront him in front of the class, I kept him in during playtimes. On such an occasion, I returned to the classroom after my coffee break in the canteen, to find him standing at the nature window sill with a penknife in his hand. The glass container no longer contained lively, wriggling tadpoles, but instead, mutilated blobs floating in a cloudy mess. He stood there glaring at me defiantly, shamefaced and near to tears.

What would be the best way to cope with this situation? For some time I had realised that here was a very confused and unhappy boy. This incident would make him even more unpopular with his classmates. They would expect me to punish him severely but I could think of no form of punishment that would bring a satisfactory result. As it was, without friends, he was happier staying in than going out to play, and being reprehended had no effect on him.

'I have no idea why you did this, Gethin, and I am not even going to ask. You know that the other boys will give you a hard time, and that can be your punishment.'

He was now sobbing loudly.

I went out to the cloakroom and brought in a bucket.

'Look, this time I will help you. I am going to blow the whistle and we'll all gather in the infants' classroom for a singing lesson. Meanwhile, you'll go down to that pool and hopefully, you'll find some tadpoles that have not yet changed into frogs. Empty that mess down the outside drain and when we come in I expect to see tadpoles in that aquarium – and don't forget the weeds!'

Later when we returned to the classroom, the deed was done. Gethin sat at his desk and in the aquarium there were tadpoles, fewer in number but far better developed specimens than the others, but no one noticed.

It so happened that the next scripture lesson dealt with the time that Jesus spent in the wilderness being tempted by the devil, which was quite appropriate under the circumstances. I was anxious not to frighten the youngsters with the concept of a devil with horns and cloven feet. Such an image had haunted me in my childhood so I tried another approach.

'We all have good thoughts and bad thoughts inside us and sometimes we are tempted to do things that are really wicked, even though we know it is wrong!'

'Like letting down Nurse Morfudd's tyres, miss?'

'Yes, suddenly, without warning, we find ourselves doing something that will hurt others. I remember the time when it happened to me, and I felt so unhappy and guilty afterwards.'

'Will you tell us about it, miss?'

'Well, when I was a little girl, I used to stay with my grandparents and my grandfather was very proud of his garden. One day when we were in the orchard he said to me, "On this young tree I am growing a special apple. You can pick apples from any other tree but not this one."

'Every time I passed that tree, I wished I could taste that special apple. I watched it change from a pale green to a lovely pinkish colour, as a rosy blush spread all over it. One morning when that apple was fresh with morning dew, suddenly a little voice inside me said, "He said you were not supposed to pick the apple, but he didn't say you couldn't have a little bite." I fetched a box from the shed, stepped on to it, reached for the branch, carefully held the apple and I bit through the skin.'

'Oh-h-h!!' from the children.

'It was very hard and very sour, and I felt terrible! My grandfather was very cross and I was sent to bed in disgrace.

'Now Jesus was in the wilderness for forty days and forty

nights. He was very hungry and thirsty and three times the devil came to tempt him, but Jesus was strong and he said, "Get thee behind me, Satan," and that is what we all have to say, when we are tempted to behave badly.'

I didn't glance in Gethin's direction, but he knew that there was a special message there for him.

Later when marking their books I found that their written work and crayoned illustrations were not of Jesus but of 'miss and the devil', but Gethin handed me a picture of himself with a bright red spot in his chest and an arrow to the word 'DANGER'.

'Sorry, miss,' he whispered.

After school, I sat at my desk, thinking that I had let him off lightly. I hoped that the fact we now shared a secret, might help to cement our relationship.

I had to admit that I felt compassion for him when I saw him standing there, obviously devastated. I knew how he felt, having once experienced that same feeling of shame and panic. I was only nine at the time but I would always remember those tulips. They stood like long lines of soldiers on either side of the path that led to our neighbour's front door. In a mad rebellious moment, I had crept in and cut off their heads. I remember that I was overwhelmed with guilt and remorse. I told no one, not even my brother Daniel, but my conscience troubled me for a very long time and the memory of two rows of headless tulips never left me.

23

Mrs Staley hurried in, short of breath.

'Get your skates on, gel, and follow me to the church.'

Off she went, and I followed her up the side path, through the wicker gate into the graveyard. Around the front, a grey-haired gentleman was busy weeding the gravel path that led to the church door.

'Brought Mrs Thomas, the new teacher, to meet you, Jones. Mr Jones Tircanvos be the church warden and a school governor,' she explained, 'and 'e be the one to tell you all about the church and the school. I be off to do my spring-cleaning,' and she disappeared.

'Ah well, it be time for me to take a rest anyrod. Sit you down here beside me,' and he made room on the raised grave stone. He had a gentle voice.

'The church in Gwenddwr has quite a history.' He pointed to the sloping field beyond the river. 'Look across the valley to the lower hillside opposite. See where the grassy slope is uneven. That be where the Cistercian Monks built the first priory well nigh five hundred years ago. The old folk remember when there were a pile of stones there, the remains of that ruined monastery. Of course, Henry VIII put a stop to that and when the monasteries were dissolved, the priory in Gwenddwr and its lands got seized by the crown which brought years of change.'

'How long has the present church been here?' I asked, noticing the good condition of the stone work.

'Ah well, at one time there was a plaque with the date 1790, when they used local stone and local craftsmen to build a new church and the earliest entry in the church's Register of Baptism is 1752. Come you inside,' he said. Opening the heavy church door, he pointed to the octagonal font near by.

'That goes back to the fourteenth century and be only one of the many important relics handed down and still here. The bells

89

in the tower, the two still rung on Sunday services, go back to the eighteenth century; the *Book of Common Prayer* in Welsh was printed during the reign of Queen Anne at the beginning of that century, but the silver communion chalice goes back as far as Queen Elizabeth the first.

'However, there was a real bad fire in 1875 and that caused serious damage to the building. You'll see in your school records that the school was given a week's holiday when the repairs were finished.'

'So when was the school built?' I asked.

'Well, I started school in 1880 and the school was built in 1864. In them days, there was only the one classroom and one schoolmaster teaching eighty children. Every Monday morning we had to pay him six pence for our education.'

'Goodness,' I said. 'We shouldn't grumble should we – having forty children in two classrooms and two teachers? How did he manage?'

'Well the older ones did help the younger ones and there was always the stick in the corner. We were all scared of that stick.'

He smiled – 'I'd better get on before the daylight goes.'

'Thank you very much for such an interesting talk, Mr Jones. Perhaps one day you'll come to school and talk to the children about your own schooldays?'

He didn't say 'yes' and he didn't say 'no'. He just raised his hand, smiled and left me there, at the church door.

This was my first opportunity to look around. The late afternoon sun shone through the stained glass window, above the altar, lightening the tiled surfaces of the nave and chancel. Every part of the old building was well preserved and I knew that Mrs Staley's programme of spring cleaning had already begun. At the end of each day, I was being given a running commentary, at supper time.

Walls, windows, beams had all received the de-cobweb treatment; floor tiles were to be washed down with milk to make them shine; pews in the aisles to be given the vinegar and water treatment; brass lamps, vases and candlesticks to be polished; altar cloths and runner to be carefully laundered. Everything would receive her loving care.

I wandered over to examine the organ which was to the right of the chancel. It was a simple oak structure with pedals and stops. I sat on the stool, and was examining the stops to be manipulated by hand, when Mrs Staley came bustling down the aisle.

'You'd better not be messing with them as Verona who do play every Sunday is sure to 'ave put them as she do want them. If you want to 'ave a go, you need to put your feet on that pedal board and then pedal like 'ole billyo to make the air blow through them pipes.'

This was the first time I had attempted to play an organ. Gingerly I began to pedal and move my hands over the keys. As I gained confidence the keys and pedals began to respond, and even though it was a novice performance, the strains of 'Abide with me' filled the friendly old church, and I experienced a great sense of well-being and belonging.

The next day I talked to the children about their church and its valuable contents. I was surprised to find that they had no knowledge of the age of the church or of its historic relics.

After all, this was a Church School and even though supply teachers had come and gone, it was surely the responsibility of the vicar and the different diocesan inspectors to pass on this information to the pupils.

I told them about the monastery that had been built across the way in the Fron field over five hundred years ago, about the present church built in 1790, one hundred and sixty years ago but that the Elizabethan silver communion cup and *The Book of Common Prayer* was much older.

'Do you know that the Common Prayer Book, printed over two hundred years ago was all in Welsh? What do you think that means?'

'I bet we be talkin' Welsh then miss.'

'Well, all the people of Gwenddwr at that time were speaking in Welsh, just like my village in Carmarthenshire speak Welsh now.' I pointed to the map of Wales to show where I lived.

'I had to learn English, because I could only speak Welsh when I was a little girl. Now the school inspectors would like *you* to try to learn a little Welsh, so we'll learn a few sentences as we go along, shall we?'

'Say something in Welsh, miss.'
Slowly, and with expression, I said,
'*Wel, Wel, meddai Wil wrth y wal,*
ond wedodd y wal ddim 'nôl wrth Wil.'
'What does it mean, miss?'
'Well! Well! said Wil to the wall,
But the wall said nothing back to Wil.'

They laughed and I knew they would remember the translation, if nothing else.

24

It was half past eight the next morning when Twm and Guto came hammering on Mrs Staley's door. I was just sitting down to my bacon and egg breakfast.

'The vicar be in school and 'e be wanting to see you, miss.'

What could he be wanting so early, I wondered, as I hurriedly put on my coat and followed the boys to school?

The playground was empty and in the schoolroom there was no sign of my visitor. From outside came a chorus of jollification.

'April Fool, miss!'

Mrs Staley ran out of the canteen to see what all the noise was about. 'I did wonder why all them kids were in school so early,' she said laughing.

It was obviously a planned conspiracy, I thought, noticing that most of my class were there. They were still in high spirits until playtime but soon calmed down when they came in from the playground to find clean sheets of paper and sharpened pencils on each desk.

'What's up, miss? Are we having a test?'

'Yes, this is an end-of-term test before we break up next week.'

There was immediate silence. It's amazing how the word 'test' has a paralytic effect.

'On the other side of the blackboard there are twenty sums. Fold your arms and rest your heads on the desk. I'll turn the blackboard. When I say 'look up', start work immediately.'

I gave the sign and watched their anxious upturned faces as the words written in large print registered. 'APRIL FOOL!' They gasped with astonishment and then there was great joy. I knew there would be no work after that so out we went for a game of rounders.

The Easter holidays were soon here and I went home feeling

mentally and physically exhausted. I had survived three gruelling and challenging months, but felt that I could look forward to a less stressful summer term.

I had been awakened by the melodious trills of the birds in the old apple tree outside my window. After the April showers the dripping branches sparkled with shiny raindrops and every bough was miraculously crowned with flecks of green waiting to burst through.

I love this bedroom, I thought, as I lay there in the morning sunshine gazing through the gnarled branches at my beloved Mynydd Du. Now that Sharon and Lynne were happily settled in their own room, I had once again claimed my own back bedroom full of childhood memories.

This is where I woke up in the very early hours of Christmas Day, groped my way across the landing to wake up Daniel and then together knock at Mam and Dada's door. It was always the same routine – Mam, in her voluminous cotton nightdress, carefully carrying the flickering candle and leading the procession down the stairs and Dada in striped pyjamas bringing up the rear. First into one room full of shadows – 'He hasn't been here.' Then into another – 'Not here either?' And then finally into a room transformed with paper chains, lanterns and the presents around the tinselled tree.

It was in this bed, too, that I lay awake worrying about the percentages, tap sums, train sums, all part of the oncoming scholarship examination, and of course Mrs Rhys Brynawel's tulips!

But I have a vivid memory of long before then, sitting bolt upright in the middle of the night convinced that I was going to have a baby. Charlie, a boy on holiday from South Africa who came for private lessons after school, had chased me and kissed me behind the piano; and I couldn't stop worrying. That night I lay tossing and turning, remembering a conversation I'd heard between our maid Mary Goss and her friend Getta who were reading the *Red Letter* magazine.

'I tell you, Getta, kissing ends with a baby,' said Mary. 'It says here that a flutter in the stomach is a sure sign.'

I must have slept. Suddenly I woke, overwhelmed with panic

– I could feel that flutter! I jumped out of bed and in the light of the moon I stood on the landing outside my parents' door screaming, 'I am going to have a baby.'

I chuckled, remembering their astonished reaction! Now, I could look forward to being at home once again and this time in sole charge, as my parents had agreed to go away for a much-needed rest.

Every day we prepared a packed lunch and then out we went into a world bright and welcoming. Bursts of sunshine brightened the drab stalks and the young leaves peeping through had never seemed so green. Chestnut buds thickened and shiny with life, beeches bursting into leaf, catkins and pussy willows now in their full golden glory and the dark spiky thicket, usually choked with brambles, now covered with white sprays of blackthorn blossom.

Birds rustled and chattered around us, all busy making countless journeys to and fro carrying wisps of hay, dry grass and wool from the hedgerows.

From the top of Gellicaerau we had an expansive view of the busy activities in the farms below. In the fields, newborn lambs gambolled merrily in the sunshine; newly-born calves ventured away from their mothers to explore the green pasture. Near the farm, young bullocks were waiting expectantly at the gate for their daily ration of hay.

Gruffydd John waved to us as he guided the two splendid horses that were pulling the plough. We watched them moving in straight furrows across the field below Brynchwith. In Glantoddeb they were busy emptying a cartload of manure and scattering it all over the ground. Meadows of freshly-turned earth, fragrant and brown, rolled side by side with stretches of tender green, below those ever watchful mountains. In every season this breathtaking panorama seemed to be sensitive to my every mood whether in solitude, in sadness, in disappointment or, as today, in pleasure.

Carefully we made our way down the steep slope of Gellicaerau until at the bottom, in between mounds of flamed yellow gorse, we entered my secret lane, now alive with colour. The children skipped ahead.

The first primroses had come into their own and were clustered thickly on the grassy banks on either side. Shy violets mingled with fresh green sorrel. There were pale mauve milkmaids, bright yellow cowslips and bold dandelions. Fragrant perfume filled the air.

Having left the shady lane, we came out again to open pastures and went towards the river. Nearby was the rickety wooden bridge where as children we would daringly hang from its wooden rail and dangle our legs over the dark green pool below. We followed the bank and in a shady marshy patch, we came across a small cluster of frail white anemones and the first crop of marsh marigolds.

We sat on a large grey boulder to enjoy our picnic and the air was filled with the music of the brook, the bleating of sheep and the answering cry of their lambs, the hum of insects and the chirping of birds. That was the day we heard the clear sweet call of the first cuckoo.

The weather remained fine and the days flew by. There were daily visits to the village shop, invitations from neighbouring farms to call for tea and a Friday trip across the Black Mountain to visit Auntie Bessie and Betty and Douglas who were always there to give their encouragement and support.

Mum and Dada benefitted greatly from their holiday at Llanmaes Rectory. We'd had such wonderful times there with Uncle Campbell, Auntie Gertie, cousins Joan and Nancy. Every August it had been an open house for all the cousins to have a family holiday and it was an ideal setting for having fun.

The beautiful house covered with ivy and virginia creeper had a rural setting, well back from the main road. The rooms were spacious, the windows large. A narrow winding staircase led up to the back landing from the kitchen and at the end of the long corridor that led to the bedrooms, a wide gracious staircase led down to the main hall – an ideal arrangement for chasing games and hide and seek.

So we enjoyed long summer days, lazing on the smooth green lawns, playing in the walled garden in and out of currant bushes, gooseberries, raspberries and rows of runner beans; in the orchard, full of little sweet red apples. But every morning at eleven, the family gathered for prayers in the study. Then off to the beach in Uncle Campbell's old Austin car, and he would always join us in the sea wearing his one piece swimming costume, down to the knees.

In the afternoons there were visits to parishioners, carrying baskets of fruit and vegetables from the garden to those who were old and those who were ill. Best of all were Sundays when Mary, Betty, Joan and I sat in the front pew making eyes at the choir boys, who were a handsome bunch.

25

During the first weeks of the summer term we worked hard, preparing for Diocesan Day, revising and re-enacting the stories of the Old Testament, the life of Jesus and perfecting the rendering of the 24th Psalm.

We also created new displays attempting to bring the delights of summer into our classroom. Radio lessons, poetry and pictures of the sea stimulated the children's art work; but not one pupil had ever seen the sea.

Surprisingly, John Masefield's 'Sea Fever' and Tennyson's 'Break, Break, Break', had produced pleasing results. Framed with a black felt pen and mounted on large sheets of pale coloured cards with suitable captions, they made an attractive display above the partition. I was particularly pleased with Johnny's effort. He was a dozy lad; shy, hesitant in speech and rarely shone in anything he attempted. This time he has excelled himself, I thought, as I framed his work.

The dark misshapen rocks in the angry smudgy sea captured the mood of

Break, Break, Break
on thy cold grey stones, oh sea.

'He'll be really chuffed when he sees this!' I said to Jinny as she anxiously watched me balancing on top of a ladder and precariously pinning his painting alongside the others.

Indeed, next day, Johnny blushed with pride as I pointed out his painting and we gave him a resounding clap.

Later that day, standing at my desk, having his book marked he said, looking at his painting,

'Yes, miss, it do look better upside down,'

Upside down! Startled, I now gazed at his work with new eyes. Goodness! The smudgy sea was meant to be the sky; the

98

misshapen rocks were black clouds, so the narrow strip of blue at the top was really the sea! That's what comes of mounting paintings after school. What should I do now? Ah well, I thought, it looks pretty good up there and it has given his ego a boost, so where's the harm? I only hoped he'd keep his mouth shut!

The long awaited Diocesan Day was nigh and the sun shone brightly that morning as I walked to school.

In the canteen there was a hustle and a bustle as Harold the butcher arrived with a huge leg of pork. Mrs Staley was up to her elbows in stuffing and a lovely aroma of fresh herbs welcomed me. On the counter beside the bowl of apples for apple sauce was a basket of shiny blackcurrants.

'They be growing in the garden of the Holly Bush. Too good to waste,' she said.

The Holly Bush was a derelict cottage opposite the school entrance and a constant source of free supply to our canteen, when blackcurrants, gooseberries and raspberries were in season. Like all the other extras they were there to enhance her meals and this of course was a special occasion. I had no doubt that if all these extras were charged, there would be a significant increase in our canteen accounts.

The children began to arrive, all in their Sunday best. The parents, remembering their own Diocesan Days, were making a special effort. This was my first experience, and I was beginning to realise its importance, not only to the school but to the community. No doubt the parents had read the riot act, because the air was charged with tension when they settled in the classroom.

Mrs Staley too made her contribution.

I was outside the classroom window dealing with Ray the Stores concerning his grocery delivery, when I heard the partition go up and her words came across loud and clear.

'Now if you want Mrs Thomas to stay, you got to go all out to do your best. Remember I'll be on the other side of this partition listening to every word, so look out anyone that do let 'er down!'

Ray the Stores smiled and I blushed with embarrassment.

They arrived on time. The vicar, 'Big John', was well over 6ft tall, fair-faced and bald, and with him came the diocesan inspector, short, dark and very serious.

'Mrs Thomas,' said the vicar, 'we meet for the first time.' He shook my hand and introduced me. 'Mrs Thomas is one of many supply teachers that have been coming here of late.'

The inspector smiled encouragingly, 'You have a bright, busy classroom,' he said as he addressed the class. 'Now I am going to find out how much you know and I'll be looking for bright answers.'

We sang 'All Things Bright and Beautiful' and after a short prayer he began.

'Now let me remind you that no one must call out. Just put up your hands if you know the answer and I'll give every one a chance.'

He began with the stories of the Old Testament, and he methodically moved around ensuring that every child was given an opportunity to answer correctly. When they failed on one question, he would try again. They were answering well and a forest of hands shot up each time.

Johnny was yet to give an answer and he looked flushed and anxious, when the inspector asked him, 'When Isaac was giving his blessing, how would he have known whether it was to Esau or to Jacob?'

I gave him an encouraging smile and kept my fingers crossed.

Johnny stammered, 'Cos Esau was furry and Jacob was smoozy.'

I held my breath, praying that no one would laugh, but there wasn't a sound.

'That's right,' said the inspector. 'Esau was hairy and Jacob was smooth, so when he touched them, he would know.'

'Oh kind, sensitive diocesan inspector!' I said to myself. That was my most anxious moment, and soon the first session was over and it was time for playtime and coffee.

Mrs Staley brought in the tray with a big grin on her face and her brown eyes twinkling.

'They be not doing so bad, be they vicar? – not by what I do 'ear from the other side of the partition, anyrod. Mrs Thomas 'ave worked real 'ard with them – fair do's.'

I turned away, pretending not to have heard and he said nothing.

'That's an interesting painting,' the inspector said, pointing to Johnny's masterpiece.

I cringed, realising which one.

'That's Johnny's.'

'Ah yes,' said the vicar with an amused smile – "furry and smoozy".'

'A sensitive boy that needed to be handled gently,' said the inspector and again my heart warmed to him.

They were far more lively when they trooped in after playtime and they responded enthusiastically to the questions on the New Testament. He was very thorough. He covered Jesus as a boy; Jesus in the temple; Jesus in the wilderness: John the Baptist, Jesus and his disciples. He dealt with some of the miracles and parables, and touched briefly on Palm Sunday, The Last Supper, the Crucifixion and the Ascension.

He concentrated on the older children, especially those who were leaving and hoping to be given Bishop Certificates, and they were all eager to show how much they knew.

Then came the grand finale – the 24th Psalm.

Trained by my parents, I had experience of choral speaking and the importance of emphasis, control, modulation of the voice and facial expressions. This psalm gave the opportunity to make use of these.

They stood, shoulders back, heads high:

> Lift up your heads, / Oh ye gates! /
> That the King of Glory / may come in /
> Who is this King of Glory? /
> The Lord of hosts, / He is the King of Glory.

It was a superb performance. They beamed at me with pride and I could have hugged them. I turned to the Reverend Gentlemen and said,

'These are my beloved children, with whom I am well pleased!'

Every pupil received a certificate and the eight pupils who were leaving were awarded Bishop Certificates.

Later over a delicious lunch there was great praise from the inspector.

'You'll be appointing a new head before the end of the year, won't you, John? I don't think you need to look any further.'

The vicar looked uncomfortable and said nothing.

The message was coming over loud and clear. He doesn't want me here, I thought, and my heart sank!

26

Following the diocesan inspection, we were granted a special holiday, greatly appreciated by all because it meant a day off for Builth Fair, a red-letter day in the lives of the community.

After months of isolation this was their opportunity to mix with crowds and be part of the world outside. For days beforehand the children's faces were flushed with excitement as they talked excitedly about the things they would see and do.

On the morning of Fair day, fathers, mothers, grandparents and children gathered on the square to meet the bus. I must admit I was reluctant to go, but Jinny wouldn't hear of my missing it.

'This be your chance to meet the parents. They all be wanting to meet Mrs Thomas.'

Sitting with her at the back, for the first time I was able to match parent with child. Girls and boys glanced back shyly, whispered, and mums and dads turned to greet me with broad smiles.

'See, they do like you,' she said.

The journey was a joyous occasion with country folk laughing, teasing and joking. Wherever there was a waiting passenger, the bus stopped and occasionally at farm gates waited for the latecomers, who arrived panting and puffing and carrying large baskets.

Having crossed the Twmpath, the road to Builth followed the beautiful river Wye. I had not travelled this way before and saw that it was a most desirable place to be. The banks on either side were in their springtime splendour, and from my elevated position I caught glimpses of the river in its varied moods – sometimes rippling across the stones, other times splashing against large boulders and then lying dark and still in mysterious pools.

We passed whitewashed farmhouses, stone cottages and large

manor houses all with gardens and orchards filled with billows of pink and white blossom.

We arrived to find the town teeming with people and full of the noise and bustle of Fair day. Everywhere there were stalls and side-shows and farm folk moved along slowly, hailing friends not seen for perhaps a year. Pavements were crammed with groups talking and laughing and outside every pub, menfolk, precariously hanging on to their pints, shuffled in and out through the open doors. I had never felt so alone.

The park behind the main streets resounded with the laughter and the music of the gaily-coloured roundabouts, the swing boats, the hoop-la, the shooting range and the coconut stalls. Without Sharon and Lynne, they were of little interest to me.

Beyond, the cattle mart was jammed with horse boxes, cattle lorries and pens packed with horses, cows and sheep. Farmers stood debating and arguing, some looking on with amusement and with hands deep in breeches' pockets and others leaning on their knobbly sticks. All the jollity and camaraderie served only to accentuate my own lonely situation and I wished I hadn't come. But not for long!

I walked through the fairground on my way back to the high street where I had arranged to meet Mrs Staley in the cafe for tea, and suddenly from all directions came greetings from the Gwenddwr children who were having such a wonderful time. They ran towards me, flushed with pleasure and urged me to join them at the hoop-la, the roll-a-penny, the coconut shy. How could I refuse them? Others were sailing high, waving and calling from the swing boats, and 'Look at us, miss!' came the excited cry from those astride the brightly coloured hobby-horses, as they clung tightly to the brass rod and the revolving platform gathered speed. I had no doubt they would re-live the memories of this day for the rest of the year.

27

Now that Diocesan Day was over, we were able to revert to a more varied timetable and once again enjoy the magic of the countryside and the news of the farmyard.

May had brought a riot of wild flowers and bird song. The nature sill was soon overflowing with treasures, the frogs by this time having been returned to their environment.

It was a time to observe, gather information and record the activities of the birds and hopefully make the children appreciate the great effort made by male and female to create warm, dry nests in safe places.

Mrs Staley had warned, 'Come nesting time, them boys are real devils, frightening the birds away from the nests and then stealing the eggs.'

So when we found the nests within the school boundary and the school garden, we kept careful records until the eggs were safely hatched. But most exciting of all, a pair of tawny owls were roosting in the old yew tree near the lychgate leading into the churchyard. At night we'd hear the 'te-week' of the female and 'whoot-a-hoo' of the male.

Jesse Price, who was always around when the taps ran dry, had been on call several times of late.

'Crows be building high,' he'd cry in his raucous voice. 'We are in for a dry summer, so don't waste de watta.'

But one morning he found two beautiful fluffy baby owls on the ground below the yew tree near the churchyard gate.

In he came to the classroom, a short stocky figure with laughing blue eyes, ruddy cheeks and rumpled, untidy, corn-coloured hair under his flat cap, which was always perched at the back of his head.

'Be ye wantin' to see a sight for sore eyes?' he shouted, and his shoulders shook as he chuckled with excitement. 'You got to be quiet mind, quiet as mice now!'

105

I smiled, thinking, not the best advice when looking for owls! Off we went, up the steps to the school house garden, and over to the far corner near the lychgate.

'Just you peep over the stone wall! There they be!'

Silently we watched them, pale, fluffy and bright-eyed, flapping their wings, losing their balance and falling over.

'Have they fallen out of the nest?' I whispered.

'Not fallen, shoved out by the parent owls I reckon,' said Jesse. 'They be wantin' them to start fendin' for theirselves, you see. I bet them old owls are in that tree keepin' watch. Sure to, so don't you think of touchin' them, or going near them. They be there for a purpose.'

'Look, miss, those be fish bones!'

'They be still feedin' them, any rod,' said Jesse.

'With fish?' I said, surprised.

'Ah well, come night time they do go down to the river. One do stamp on the flat stone and the other do stab the trout as they dart out in fright.'

Remembering my 'trout tickling' days, I could well imagine that happening, but it was news to me that owls went fishing.

Jesse's discovery had caused great excitement and subsequently produced exciting writing, painting and plasticine models.

I was never sure whether he always needed to deal with taps and the supply of water when he came to school for he was a regular visitor. He was the weather-wise man, who would open the classroom door and interrupt my lessons to announce in high-pitched voice,

'Rain be near, swallows be flyin' low.'

or 'It was rainin' afore seven, so it be clear before eleven.'

or 'Birds stopped singin', it'll soon be thunderin'.'

or 'No dew this mornin', so look out for rain.'

At home on weekends I took delight in dropping Jesse's pearls of wisdom at appropriate times, to the family's surprise and amusement.

The farming diary brought news of a busy time, gathering the sheep, washing and shearing. Boys came to school looking tired and dishevelled, having spent hours roaming over the hillsides looking for the sheep that had strayed to inaccessible places on rocks and in gullies. The mere sight of man and dog made them rebellious, charging in all directions and hiding in the bracken and undergrowth.

Then on a bright day with white clouds sailing across a blue sky we set out to watch the dipping. From a sloping bank above the river we had a good view of the deep pool overhung by alder trees. There was a great din of bleating, barking and shouting. Men in water up to their waists clung to the struggling ewes, passed hand to hand from the pens, and plunged each ewe into the water to remove the dirt, grit and grease; sheepdogs kept watch as the sheep were freed. They swam to the edge and staggered and slithered over the slippery stones. Everyone standing near got soaked as they shook off the water and scurried off to search for their lambs.

The womenfolk arrived with laden baskets and we went back to school. Soon, when the fleece was ready to be shorn, to make clipping easy, they would be together again. It was not only an industrious time but a social event – a time for communal activity, when at shearing time neighbours arrived to help. The ewes were dragged from the pen to the shearing shed and the men, working at the shearing benches, clipped the wool using their strong agile hands to wield the sharp shears. They worked together on one another's farms so that each small flock was shorn in a day. They always chose a fine day as wet sheep were unpleasant to shear. The soft dry fleeces were rolled up and when work was over, with stiff backs, they'd gather in the farmhouse for a well-deserved meal. It was a time for laughter and gossip.

28

So followed sunny summer days when we spent time out of doors at every opportunity. The Education Office had responded generously to my begging letters and we were now well-equipped with a new piano, a radio, art easel, and P.E. equipment including a Maypole, discarded by a neighbouring school that had closed. I had no scruples in asking for more than our share, as Gwenddwr school had been left without for years.

For the sake of stability they had requested that I stayed for a whole year until the school was handed over to the authority, so 'Make hay while the sun shines' had turned out to be a beneficial policy.

Walking to Erwood on Fridays to catch my train was now a pleasure. The scent of the wild rose and honeysuckle in the hedgerows and the whirr of insects was all around me. Looking forward to my weekend, I'd walk with sprightly step, along lanes where hedges and verges were garlanded with red campion, where the twinkling blue speedwell peeped through the grass, and pink and purple foxgloves grew bright and high.

Then to the open spaces of the Twmpath, to the haunting call of the curlew and the mournful mew of the buzzards. Once again, waves of golden purse mingled with purple wild heather and fresh green bracken. For some weeks after a bleak winter and gorse fires, the mountain road had meandered through bleak and decaying scenery, where the wild mountain ponies stared disconsolately at their charred surroundings. Now they nibbled fresh green shoots, but always keeping an eye on the young foals, some strong enough to gambol and play, and others lying in the green ferns, viewing that new world with dark bright eyes.

At times like these I was able to quell the uncertainties within me and feel confident that the future was promising. But then came the Friday before the Whitsun break, when I walked that way dispirited and with a heavy heart.

I had no premonition or worries on Thursday evening, when I was preparing the schoolroom for the Governors' meeting. I had no doubt that they would discuss the results of the diocesan inspection which would be in my favour and the school looked bright and busy. It was not likely that they would discuss the headship.

A new head was to be appointed in the autumn term and it was now agreed that the post would advertise for a headmistress and not a headmaster, which would give me the opportunity to apply when the time came.

I went to bed feeling light-headed and looking forward to going home on the morrow. The loud footsteps, the banging on the door and Jones the Cwm's gravelly voice disturbed my light sleep.

'Bad news, Jinny!'

'Wot be ye blatherin' about, Jones?'

'Vicar says she be too young to be headmistress.'

'I did neva' 'ear such twaddle.'

'Onest to God, Jinny, 'e be real serious. With two young 'uns and no 'usband it would be too much for lass to take on. Anyrod, 'e do want a man there to mind the garden and do repairs, 'e says.'

Her voice rose to a loud crescendo, 'I did never 'ear the like. So it be an odd job man 'e be wanting, not a good teacher! Mrs Thomas 'as worked like a good 'un all year. She don't stop from morn 'til night. "Ye be fair wore out, gel," I say to 'er but she don't listen one bit, all because she be workin' for a home for her children. You call yourselves Christians? I got no time for you!'

'Oh fair do's, Jinny, I like the lass. Don't be mad at me.'

'Mad! I am tampin mad! Be off with you!'

'No cup o'tea, Jinny?'

'Not tonight, or ever!' and the door slammed.

I lay there in my bed, feeling numb and cold. My fingers and feet were icy. I could hardly feel them. I snuggled seeking comfort. The white cotton sheets had a cold, ivory smell which I identified with the emptiness within me.

What had it all been for? That belief that every sacrifice was worthwhile to achieve my goal. The difficult days in school which had driven me to my lowest ebb; the sleepless nights, when, feeling drained and dispirited, I had felt I could not carry on; the loneliness and heartbreak in being parted from the children.

Everyone thought I had taken leave of my senses when I had chosen to come here. Why had I been so obsessed by that driving force within me? Why had I been so sure? In my vulnerable state had it, after all, been one great delusion on my part?

Yet I had continued to believe that this was my destiny. I had been determined to overcome every setback and confront every new challenge, and it had paid dividends. Indeed, since April, everything had been going so well. I had dared to believe that my cherished hopes would be fulfilled because good fortune had smiled on me in so many ways.

But I was wrong. I had failed! Why should it be? Did I not deserve to succeed? What could I do? Had I the will or the spirit to try again elsewhere?

Tossing and turning, the anguished thoughts that mulled in my head could not be stilled.

As dawn broke, the rising sun threw flickering lights across the room, and suddenly the silence of daybreak was broken by a summer chorus of song. The sweet, tranquil notes of the blackbird were soon joined by the wide range of song from the wrens, the thrushes, the hedge sparrows and others, heralding the beginning of a summer's day, but I was unaffected and the magic outburst of song failed to raised my spirits. Indeed the mournful cry of the curlew during the night had been more in tune with the sadness within my soul.

It had been a night of dejection and soul searching, but early morning brought more positive thinking. I must not allow my disappointment to affect others. I would need to come to terms with my present position. My post as County Supply would keep me here until December. I had saved money for furniture which could now be used to buy a car. That would not only solve my transport problems, but it would open up opportunities for the future. All these plans would mean considerable delay in finding a home, and having Sharon and Lynne with me, which I wanted above all things. Meanwhile I must continue to put on a brave face and stay the course.

The door opened and Jinny brought in my morning cup of tea. She looked at me anxiously.

'Biddy bach, I can see that you be upset. 'E be talking through that big clerical black 'at of 'is, 'e be, but it baint be over yet, you wait an' see! Just ye keep yer chin up, gel.'

I looked at her with affection. She had been a good friend to me. How many times had she been there to give her support and encouragement when I had been in the doldrums? I would not have survived without her.

29

The remaining weeks of term allowed no time for brooding. A series of tests for all ages would assess individual progress. Four were of school leaving age, but under the new agreement with the Education Authority, the other five over eleven would go to the secondary school in Builth Wells. Hopefully, the two girls, Ann and Freda, would be of standard to be admitted to the Grammar stream.

We had weathered the storm of those difficult winter months and even though the older lads were not angels by any description, we had a far better understanding and I was grateful for their support. I would miss their quick-witted humour and their contribution to our nature diary and farming news. I had learned a great deal from them.

In September, my class would be of a different composition, far younger, all over eleven years having been transferred and children of seven being moved up from the infants. Record cards, attendance registers, meal registers, official forms and correspondence were awaiting attention, but in spite of all the chores there was still time for nature walks and rambles.

We walked down the lane towards the mill in the drowsy warmth of a summer afternoon to the music of wasps and bees as they buzzed around us. In a dark pool in front of the mill the silver trout darted under the flat stones, their flitting dark shadows mingling with the reflection of the overhanging branches. The boys took off their shoes and socks and proved to be experts at catching the elusive creatures. Back to school we went, carrying twigs threaded with silvery fish, and I had trout for my tea!

During the last week of the summer term, having cleared out desks, tidied cupboards, stripped walls of charts and paintings, we had our school outing to Pantllyn.

Janet Roberts and I were up early helping Mrs Staley to

112

prepare the packed lunches which would replace the mid-day meal. There was home-boiled ham, and cheese and lettuce sandwiches; vegetable pasties and apples for everyone and then large containers of *pwdin bara* – chunks of spiced currant bread-pudding.

We set off carrying baskets of packed lunches and bottles of water. The sun shone and the birds sang as we left the village road and followed a country lane passing farm houses where black and white collies barked excitedly at the crowd of noisy unexpected visitors.

With raised voices the children chattered and laughed. We left the lane and went through gates into fields among thistles, cowpats and 'oomtitimps'. Older boys and girls carried the little ones on their backs and we relied on them to show us the way to their chosen destination.

'Not long now, miss!'

Soon we arrived at the wide open spaces of the mountains, dotted with wild ponies and grazing sheep and ahead of us a large glistening lake set in a landscape of sweeping hills and green pastures. This then was Pantllyn, the place they had chosen for our school picnic. It was beautiful.

'There it be, miss!'

Ruddy cheeks and bright eyes glowed with pleasure. Then off they went shouting with joy, running, skipping and gambolling towards the water. We followed and amongst purple vetch, old man's beard and long slender grasses we set out our hampers in a hollow near the lake. Scattered around, everyone was having a great time leap-frogging, somersaulting, attempting hand-stands and showing their expertise at the lakeside, playing ducks and drakes and spinning the small flat stones across the shining water.

A sharp blow on the whistle brought everyone running, all eagerly looking forward to their picnic lunch, but first we made crowns of ferns and as we sat around in a circle we must have looked like a pow-wow of indians as our green fronds waved in the breeze.

There followed an afternoon of sports, ball games and singing games, and jubilant cheers echoed throughout the valley. Before

113

setting off, back to school, they were glad to rest in the cool bracken and enjoy a snack of the spiced currant *pwdin bara.*

The surface of the lake looked like silver in the afternoon sunshine. There were ripples and plops as the fish surfaced in the clear water.

'What would you say if that ripple got bigger and bigger and a beautiful girl with golden hair stood up in the middle of the lake?'

In reply to my question they rolled in the grass, laughing scornfully.

'You can laugh, but that's what happened to a young farmer called Gwyn.'

Now there was silence!

'Tell us about it, miss.'

'Well, the lake was called Llyn-y-Fan near my home in Carmarthenshire. It is said that when Gwyn was looking after his sheep near the lake, this lovely maiden appeared, and he shared his bread and cheese with her. "I must be dreaming," he thought.

'But it happened again and again and every time she looked more beautiful than ever.

' "Next time, I shall ask her to marry me," said Gwyn. So he dressed up in his Sunday best and down he went to the lake.

'This time, when she stood up in the silvery water, he put out his hand and said, 'Come to me and be my wife.' To his joy, she walked towards him and together they walked towards the farm.'

The children's faces were wreathed in smiles.

'Ah, but that was not all; following her, came cattle and sheep of the very best breed so not only did he have a beautiful wife, but with this stock he became a rich farmer too.

'So you, boys, who are leaving school never know your luck. It might happen to you one day.'

They laughed. 'Oh miss,' but the little ones gazed at the lake, not knowing what to believe.

Indeed on that summer's day there was magic in the air and one could believe that anything was possible. A thought crossed

114

my mind – 'Anything?' but I quickly dismissed that hope which I found so difficult to relinquish.

It had been such a wonderful day, with so much to see and hear: the scent of summer all around us, butterflies fluttering, the high grasses full of crickets, the croak of frogs in the rushes and in the blue sky birds were rising, swooping and turning with haunting cries.

We arrived in the village, weary and worn out at the end of our long walk, but it had been a memorable, happy day for us all.

30

I arrived home for the long summer break, ever mindful of my obligations to my parents and my children. I would make up to them for the time I had been away, but I needed time to adjust to a period without school work.

The drive, the challenge and the enthusiasm of the past seven months had kept my adrenaline high. Now that my plans for the future were more uncertain than ever, I could well feel low in spirit and revert to past feelings of despair and failure.

Kahlil Gibran wrote:

> In keeping yourself with labour, you are in truth living life . . .
> For to be idle is to become a stranger into the seasons and step out of life's procession . . .
> And I say that life is indeed darkness save when there is urge . . .

So it was with me! I had need to keep myself busy with no time to brood.

I was, therefore, apprehensive when on arrival I was greeted by the news that my parents had booked a seaside holiday for us all in Aberystwyth, where in past years I had enjoyed happy childhood holidays and carefree student days. Finding myself there years later as a single parent with two little girls would only serve to accentuate my solitary plight.

However, I didn't have the heart to tell them how I really felt. Bubbling with excitement Sharon and Lynne skipped around, laughing and talking breathlessly.

'We'll play on the sands; we'll have buckets and spades; we'll paddle in the sea. Nana says we'll see Punch and Judy.'

Lynne jumped up and down, nodding her head and repeating 'sands', 'sea', 'Judy'.

Everything was already packed and off we went to Aberystwyth. As soon as we approached the sea front, memories came flooding back and I stepped back in time.

It was all there – the strong smell of slimy wet seaweed; the thudding sound of the crashing waves on the coarse pebbly beach; seagulls swooping, screeching and squabbling; the promenade full of holiday makers in bright attire greeting and hugging friends not seen since last summer; elderly couples sitting on the green benches, holding hands and gazing out to sea.

They were still there, these places that held special childhood memories – the slipway where we met the mackerel boats every morning; the jetty where at eleven we daily sang action songs with the Salvation Army. Daniel always longed for a tambourine and I wished I had a poke bonnet. Little did he know that years later he, as a boy soprano, and Mam as Madam Jennie would be the main artistes in a Sunday Night Concert at the King's Hall across the road. I was a 'fresher' that year and when their names appeared on the posters, I held my head up high as I passed by to my lectures.

Yes, I had wonderful memories of student days at the college by the sea. It had been an exciting world of Saturday hops, college *soirées* and debates, rag week and college balls, red and green striped blazers and long college scarves; in winter, being blown by the wind from Carpenter Hall to lectures and dodging the forceful spray at high tide; on calm evenings, strolling towards Constitution Hill with a current boyfriend and 'Kicking the bar'. I suppose at that time I believed that my life would develop in one bright line and I did not anticipate the many pitfalls on the way.

For the sake of my family, I made the effort to keep smiling and participated in all the pleasurable activities of a seaside holiday – building sandcastles, searching for pebbles and shells, paddling and jumping over the waves that chased us to the edge of the surf; the children's concerts in the bandstand and, the favourite time of all, licking an ice cream cornet and watching Punch and Judy.

As I watched them giggling and shouting with excitement against a background of sand, sea and blue sky, I thought to myself, I must never let my disappointments spoil their lives. For, indeed, during that week, whether on the promenade, the beach or the town, the sight of young mums and dads enjoying their holiday with their youngsters, brought great heartache and I knew that for me the way ahead would be very lonely.

'Do you remember our Salvation Army sing-songs, Daniel?' I asked a week later when he was driving us to St Clears where he lived with his wife Pat and baby son Carl.

'Remember? of course I do!' and he burst into song.

> If you get there, before I do
> Look out for me, for I'm coming too.
> Away far beyond Jordan,
> We'll meet in that beautiful land!

Soon we were going through our repertoire of action songs, waving our arms as we sang, to the surprise of drivers passing by.

Sharon and Lynne clapped their hands in delight.

I looked at my brother with affection. He had a beautiful baritone voice and he looked like Robert Taylor. He had given up a teacher's training course and was now a successful representative with Michelin, with a fashionable car, a J.E.A., which he had christened, 'Jane Eynon Adorable', because his pet name for his wife was Jane.

Pat was a nurse and her father, locally known as Pop Eynon the Butcher, also ran the Butcher's Arms in St Clears, once a favourite haunt of Dylan Thomas. Indeed, it has been said that Pop Eynon could well have been the inspiration for Butcher Beynon in *Under Milk Wood*. Pat would recall the times she returned from school to find Dylan in his corner sitting with his pint and scribbling away. His framed photograph was still there on the wall, I noticed.

The hot summer weather stayed with us throughout our stay so there were more days on the beach at Pendine. There we played in far softer sand and unlike Aberystwyth, the sea was so tranquil, it was safe to wade in, join hands and bob up and down in the waves. There were also rock pools which we could safely explore.

The yellow beach stretched out for ever, flat and damp and there Daniel gave me my first driving lessons. It was here that

Amy Johnson once landed unexpectedly causing great excitement. When the news spread, people from different parts of the country, who had cars, travelled over night to see her, and I remember that my parents set out at dawn, which would give them time to get to Pendine and be back in time for school.

We had good days with Daniel and Pat and baby Carl that year, and several other happy holidays in subsequent years. Very early on, as a baby in his pram, we observed Carl's fascination for wild birds and this interest developed as a toddler, and again as a young lad who tended injured birds in a refuge that he created in the back garden. From all over the area, wounded birds were brought to his wildlife hospital, and he became known as the 'bird boy'.

We little thought then that one day he would become internationally renowned as a conservationist and ornithologist, who would be invested with The Order of the Golden Ark for his life-time work in saving rare birds from extinction – such as the Mauritian Kestrel, the Pink Pigeon and the Parakeet, the world's rarest parrot. He was born with the gift and thinking of him I often wonder whether there could be some truth in re-incarnation after all!

31

So the days passed by and soon only a week of my holiday remained. A week when we needed to settle down to a routine and help the children to accept that, soon, I would have to leave.

One of the advantages of living in the school house was having the use of the large rectangular playground on the other side of the garden wall. Where else would Daniel and I have had the space to race around on roller skates, ride our bicycles, play tennis, football and cricket? All these activities we could enjoy in our own private area within sight of the Mynydd Du in all its moods and dramatic splendour.

Sharon and Lynne skipped around the same playground now, happy to be in familiar surroundings; making use of the space, showing off on their tricycles; taking long walks around the quadrangle – Sharon pushing her pram full of dolls and Lynne pushing Neddy on wheels with her teddy astride.

They are just as happy here as they were at the seaside, I thought, listening to their merry chatter.

As for me, this tranquil scene was my haven. At the top of the school yard I relaxed in a deck chair, facing the rolling velvety slopes and the dark shadows in the crevasses. On a clear summer afternoon, the hairpin mountain road changing direction at Tro'r Gwcw, Cuckoo bend, stood out clearly and those rising peaks loomed nearer than ever. It had become a regular routine to sing to little Sir Echo. When the children heard the answering call 'Hello, Hello', they too believed he'd 'come over and play' one day, just as I had done all those years ago.

Every morning we climbed the wooden stile to look for mushrooms in the hay field on the other side of the school yard. The children shouted with delight as they spied and pounced on each pearly white treasure and soon their little baskets were full.

I gazed around remembering haymaking times which had brought the farm to our doorstep. We would listen for the whirring noise of the hay machine and run to the stile to watch the horse plodding round and round as swathes of rich grass and a profusion of wild flowers fell to the ground. Next day there was exciting activity as menfolk, womenfolk, servants and children arrived with hand-rakes. They worked all day turning the damp hay to dry in the sun and the breeze, before raking into rows and later stacking into hay cocks. During those days they'd often work all day long until sunset, but there were meal breaks when they gathered around the laden baskets full of farm fare and delicious home-made ginger beer. The young people fooled around diving into the hay cocks. Daniel and I were always included and laughter and merrymaking filled the air. Then when we knew it was time to bring in the *gambo*, the two-wheeled cart, to carry the load of hay, we'd rush to meet it as it trundled its way to the meadow and there was always an offer of a bumpy ride. We'd cling to the bars and corner points and shake all over as the large wooden gambo wheels rumbled over the rough ground. After many trips to the barn when the loads of hay were roped down, it was soon the last load. I remember the stillness in that field, as Daniel and I climbed the stile, regretting that the excitement of haymaking was over for another year.

After the crops of hay had been taken in, this field, now covered in fresh green grass soaked with early morning dew, was always a place for mushrooms.

That last night, sleep eluded me. Having to leave the children on the morrow would be more stressful than ever. During the past weeks I had managed to suppress my anxieties and my feelings of despair and disappointment. Instead, I had found the energy to focus on the joy of being with Sharon and Lynne and see to their needs and desires. We had enjoyed precious days of happiness.

Now that the summer holiday was over, I faced the coming term with little hope. The vicar's decision had shattered my illusions.

My heart sank at bedtime when Lynne, with her spoon in the

air and her little rosebud mouth circled with milk, looked at me appealingly.

'Mami, no go away.'

Sharon looked tense and anxious and said hesitatingly, 'Now Lynne, Nana has told us that Mami has to go away to find us a home. Then we'll all be together, won't we, Mami?'

What was going on in her little head? I wondered. She never mentioned her father or asked for him but she hadn't forgotten. Even at that age she cared enough not to cause me distress, but how was this heartbreaking situation affecting her?

I was making every effort to blank out these memories but at times like these it was impossible.

I lay awake staring at the branches of the old apple tree, now dark elongated shadows under the starry sky. Drowsily, I drifted in and out of sleep. I woke suddenly. I had a dream, a frighteningly vivid dream!

Sharon and I were in the hay field. The sky was very blue, the grass was very green, and we were picking mushrooms. Suddenly, the sky darkened, and pounding towards us came the most ferocious bull I had ever seen!

Hand in hand, we ran in panic towards the stile. We stumbled and fell. There was no escape! But, racing by, the bull reached the stile and with a roguish wink, 'I raced you two,' he bellowed.

I'd heard shaggy dog stories and I suppose I could describe this as a shaggy bull dream. Was there a message in this dream for me? I wondered. Ever mindful of doom and gloom was I being reminded by the old bull that every cloud has a silver lining?

I would not let this setback beat me. Why give in to the grief of failure? Far better to accept my situation and make new plans for the future, but I was no longer ready to sleep.

With raised spirits, I lit the candle and began to write.

> Gleefully she pounced on pinky white mushrooms
> Peeping through wet green grass –
> A sunny day, a lovely day.
> We were picking mushrooms, my daughter and I.

A blackening cloud in a blue sky,
A shadow on the now fading dew –
A grey day, a frightening day.
We ran for our lives
My daughter and I.

Hooves pounding, hearts bursting
Too late, too late, I threw myself across my child
And we waited for death
My daughter and I.

But thundering past, he reached the stile
And with one loud bellow
'I raced you two', he cried.
And we laughed, my daughter and I.

I realised that I was feeling much better. A little therapy does one a power of good, I thought, as I blew out the candle and settled down for a few hours' sleep.

32

Next morning, I caught an early train from Llangadog. The family came with me to the station and I stood at the window waving until they were specks on the platform. It was an emotional time for us all, and now in the privacy of a closed compartment I was able to give vent to my pent-up emotions.

But not for long! I had made up my mind to face the coming term with raised spirits and think positively about the future.
We arrived at Erwood in good time. Setting out from the station to walk over the Twmpath to Gwenddwr was no hardship on such a golden September day.

I crossed the bridge and looked down at the wide, silver Wye, today calm and seemingly resting on the pale, flat, ridge rocks that edged the river bank.

Having crossed the road I followed the winding country lane to the Twmpath. Pink clouds of willow herb decked the sloping banks, and butterflies fluttered midst the nettles. Misted spider-webs festooned the hawthorn hedges decked with red berries and all around me there was a humming murmur of bees.

The steep climb around the corner made me puff and blow and soon I came out to the open spaces of the moorland. The great sea of green ferns formed a soft background to the blaze of yellow gorse. Above, young buzzards joined their parent birds in gliding on unseen breezes and exploring the vastness of the sky.

This would be a wonderful place to fly a kite, I thought. Where would I be able to buy a kite, I wondered? I must make enquiries. It would be such a wonderful treat, to bring my class here and let them watch a kite flying high and free. We could still expect some fine days in September and October, so the sooner the better, I thought, as I walked towards the village.

Mrs Staley greeted me with a big smile, her brown eyes twinkling.

'It be good to see you, Mrs Thomas.'

She placed before me a plate of sandwiches and a cup of tea. I realised I was hungry.

'Sit ye down, and I'll give ye all the news. Then I be off to Builth. Eddie the Cwm is givin' me a lift.

'Well, them big nobs from Brecon did come. Thank God, I did finish the cleaning before they did come, but it be a close shave. It was on a Friday I did say to Jesse Price, "This cloakroom do still look dingy after all my scrubbin'. I 'av a mind to give it a lick."

'Jesse said, "Maudie Church 'ouse 'ave been doin' a bit of decoratin'. I reckon she 'ave some distemper to spare."

So off 'e did go to ask Maudie and indeed she did give me enough to do them walls, bless 'er. Then Jesse did bring green paint for the rails and pegs. It do look real champion now. Didn't you notice w'en you come in?'

'Yes, indeed, Mrs Staley everything looks squeaky clean.' I gazed about noticing the sparkling windows, the glistening brass lamps and there was a pungent smell from the richly polished oak desks.

No money came from the church for decoration and alterations but by begging, borrowing and spending her own hard-earned wages, she had continued to care for the school, taking pride in its appearance.

'Anyrod, I did say to Jones, "Wot news, Jones?" '

"Ah well the county be takin' ova' the school but the school house still belong to we."

'No talk of the new head then,' I said.

'No, it be up to them now, I reckon. So, gel, I do 'ave a feelin' in my old bones.'

I smiled but I said nowt!

There was much to be done. To ensure a good start to the term it was essential to have books, materials and work cards to hand. The classrooms too needed to be bright and busy to welcome the pupils back to school. It would be a very different school without the older children. The seven-year-olds moving up from the infants would feel shy and insecure in their new environment. Teaching them would give me the insight into our infant methods, indicating whether our approach was effective and where there needed to be changes. During the year I had been so involved in coping with my own class, that regretfully I had not given Janet Roberts the support she deserved. However, she would be with us for another school year and having the same teachers for the next term would give the school stability.

The young entrants from outlying farms would need special attention. They would be hesitant in speech and lacking in confidence, having had very little experience in communicating with others. After all, the work on the farm went on from early morning until sunset, so there was little time for small talk. It was therefore very important to link our teaching with the activities which were meaningful to them. From the beginning, crayoning, painting and plasticine activities and toy models linked with their own experiences, would lead to free expression in speaking and working; reading cards would be based on 'sounds' linked with pictures of farm animals. Similarly counting activities, linking counting apparatus with counting animals, comparing groups, and introducing number language such as big cow, small cow, more cows, fewer cows in preparation for addition and subtraction. Given confidence and already having experience, they could be encouraged to make up their own number stories. How easy it would be for a youngster who had grown up on a farm to describe a number picture (2+1=3) or using animal plastic models. 'Two brown cows and one black cow, so I see three cows.'

Goodness, I had only been back a couple of hours and I was already involving myself in future plans, when there was still much to be done to get myself organised for the morrow.

Janet Roberts would not be back until the evening, but I could arrange to have a sing-song with the whole school after assembly, to give her time to prepare her classroom. Fortunately, the usual chores of tidying cupboards, sharpening pencils, cutting paper etc. had already been done at the end of term so it was only a matter of putting up friezes and pictures and setting out books and apparatus.

I spent a busy afternoon getting the attendance and meal registers organised so it was four o'clock before I had time to open the large, sealed envelope containing official letters and forms. Obviously, the beginning of a year brought extra correspondence, I thought, as I began to sort through the thick pile. It would take hours to wade through this lot, so I decided to separate the urgent from the non-urgent. I came across a small sealed envelope addressed to 'Mrs Thomas' and marked 'Confidential', probably informing me of the change in school status. I began to read:

> The Education Dept.,
> County Offices,
> Brecon.
> 1st September, 1951

Dear Mrs Thomas,

At the last meeting of the District Education Committee, it was decided to offer you the post of Headmistress at Gwenddwr V.P. School, to take effect from the 1st January, 1952.

Please acknowledge receipt of this letter and let me know whether you accept.

Yours faithfully,

> Deiniol Williams
> Chief Education Officer.

33

The words dance and blur on the page. The blood rushes to my face. My ears are throbbing and my heart is thumping. I can't stop shivering and my teeth are chattering. I wrap my arms around me trying to control my emotions. In the silence of the classroom, the school clock on the wall ticks louder than ever.

I know I am in shock! I had driven myself to the physical limit to achieve this headship which would provide a future and a home for me and the children.

I had been at my lowest ebb those weeks after he left us. Every dream, every hope had been shattered and anxiety for the future had paralysed my whole being. I was broken in spirit, but then after a period of grief had come the will to succeed.

Now at last after all the sacrifices, the struggle, the frustrations and the disappointments, the goal is within my grasp. My dream is almost realised. What is the matter with me? I should be whooping with joy, but I just feel emotionally drained! Why am I finding it so difficult to accept that all my effort is being rewarded? This must be a delayed reaction to the trauma of the past eighteen months, I think to myself, as I wearily lean on the table and rest my head on my arms. I am physically exhausted!

After a while, I get up and in a daze I take the school house key from its secret hiding place. I open the front door and step into the parlour. I smell the mustiness of the fallen soot in the red-tiled Victorian grate. I move from room to room, trying to rekindle the feelings of anticipation experienced on that first occasion. Today in the grey of an autumn afternoon, everything looks neglected and forlorn.

I am ever mindful of the flaky ceilings, the deep cracks in the drab, distempered walls and the thick, lumpy brown paint on the beams.

I begin to climb the creaky stairs. A sudden shaft of autumn sunshine slants through the small landing window, filling the stairway with a welcoming glow. I rest on the window sill. The warmth of the sun on my back seeps through my body, slowly bringing me back to normality. Still in a daze, I look around. To my right is the door that will lead to Sharon and Lynne's bedroom. I open the door and feel stirrings of excitement within me. It is true! With almost no warning, I have come out into the sunshine. I am nearly, nearly there!

'Be you in here, Mrs Thomas?'

Mrs Staley is back already! I realize I had left the front door open. I go bounding down the stairs. She stands there in the parlour – a neat little figure in her best blue-grey coat.

'I do come to lock up and I did wonder!' she says looking at me quizzically.

Laughing through my tears, I hug her.

'I couldn't have done it without you, Mrs Staley, never, ever!'

'What ever be the matter, Mrs Thomas?'

'I got the job!'

She stands there gob-smacked.

'Got the job?' Her voice rose excitedly.

'There was a letter in my mail. Starting January.'

In shock, she sits herself down on the creaky stairs.

'Well I never! Well I never did hear the like! Didn't I say? Them bones of mine, they do never let me down!' She hugs herself with joy, rocking to and fro.

Looking around, she walks through to the living room.

'Well gel, in that case, the sooner we get crackin' the better.'

'But Mrs Staley, I don't expect they'll let me have the house until January.'

'Don't you be frettin', gel, they be wantin' rent. It be only one pound every month. It won't break ye!'

I gasp – 'Only a pound!'

'Any rod, no way be they wantin' to pay for any work that got to be done so it be up to ye and me. Wotever we can't do, we do call in Jesse! That black range will be 'is first job, I reckon. We'll be needin' a fire, and them skirtins will need a strip of wood to cover them gaps to stop the mice gettin' in. It be a good, sound building,' she says, walking around. 'Not a sign of dampness anywhere! Them beams, doors and window frames do need chipping, scraping and sanding. A dose of Rentokil to treat that woodworm too,' she adds, noticing the pin-holes on the timber.

'All them loose bits on the ceilings and walls must come off and we'll be needing some adamant to fill in them cracks. That be a form of plaster we do use. After we done all them jobs it be a matter of washing everything down with sugar soap, and sizing walls and ceilings. Then we can start paintin' and decoratin'.'

She looks at me. 'If we do get our skates on, you could be in by Christmas, Mrs Thomas,' and her little face beams with pleasure.

I marvelled at her energy and her lively mind. Within minutes she had assessed what was needed to be done and reeled off the jobs. To me, never having attempted work of this kind, the task ahead was momentous, but how could I fail with such a Trojan by my side? She would be my gaffer, my foreman and a labourer combined and I would be her willing apprentice.

34

That night in my bed, I mulled over the events of the day which had miraculously changed my situation. The cost of making the school house habitable, the furniture, furnishings and all household equipment would soon deplete my savings.

So far, I had avoided consulting a solicitor but I would now need to act positively. I had not given any consideration to seeking maintenance and I had not received any. In no way had he shown any concern for our situation. Christmas and birthdays had come and gone, but there were no greetings or gifts from him for Sharon and Lynne.

Along the grapevine came the news that he was successful in his teaching career, having a good relationship with his peers and pupils. Why then could he not remember his children? I had continued to feel compassion for him. I truly believed that his irrational and disturbed behaviour during our years together had been a post-traumatic reaction to his war time experiences, but now I felt resentful too.

When he left, I was a pathetic specimen crushed in mind and spirit. He would have presumed that we would live with my parents indefinitely. I realised that it would give me great satisfaction to inform his solicitor, that having been appointed headmistress of a primary school, I was now in a position to set up home for Sharon, Lynne and me. I had proved that we could survive without him and I was 'chuffed' at my spirited reaction!

As Mrs Staley correctly depicted, the vicar and church wardens were only too glad to let me take over the house immediately and by the end of the week it had all been arranged.

When I arrived home on the Friday, they were busy preparing for the whist drive. My parents and the children were astounded and delighted when I told them my news, and that evening in the school room, Dada proudly announced,

'I know you'll all be glad to hear that Mair has been appointed headmistress of Gwenddwr School and will be setting up home in the school house.'

Everyone clapped and beamed with delight and my eyes filled with tears. They had all been so supportive and I was so grateful to them.

Back in Gwenddwr, we decided it would be to our advantage to let Jesse get on with his jobs before we got started. With Mrs Staley's help I made a list of all the materials, containers, brushes and tools we'd need for renovating, cleaning and decorating and Jesse collected the order from Owens in Builth Wells, and he added his own requirements.

During those first weeks he repaired the kitchen range, cleaned the chimneys; repaired and replaced some of the skirtings; re-fitted the windows to exclude draughts, and a few of the painted sledge and thumb latched doors which needed re-hanging.

I had paid him for all the materials but I was anxious to pay him adequately for all his work.

'Don't you be frettin' yourself, lass. The money don't mean nothin' to me. I do just fill in time between my other jobs.'

It worried me even more when I overheard Mrs Staley and Jesse in the school canteen.

'Any jobs we do, do save Mrs Thomas money. She do need every penny to set up home for the littl' uns.'

'Aye, me and thee will see she be alright,' said Jesse.

I could see that dealing with the pair of them was going to be a problem, and when the work was done, I would seek advice and make sure that they were compensated for all their hard work.

So began a very busy autumn term.

The new children settled well in both classrooms and soon we were back to normal routine, following our programme of work in mathematics and language, making full use of all new apparatus and equipment. The attractively illustrated story books, topic books, and radio and follow-up creative activities, enhanced the interest in other subjects.

It was an exciting time for nature news, with the table full of the harvest of the hedgerows and woodlands. We were asked to decorate the font for the Harvest Festival, so on a Friday we set out to gather long sprays of elder, rowan, hawthorn and the wild rose, all now rich in blue-black, or orange, or scarlet, or crimson berries, which created an attractive display around the ancient grey font.

Every day brought new change and soon the countryside was ablaze with colour. A hard morning's work was often rewarded with an afternoon nature walk.

When the sun-warmed blackberries were right for picking we went searching the hedgerows, already splashed with gold by the first tints of autumn. Peeping through the brambles we found shining black clusters. We carefully picked the juicy fruit and we soon had more than enough for Mrs Staley's blackberry pies.

'Next time you do go,' she whispered to me, 'make sure you do head towards the coppice. We be needing loads of kindlin', once we do get into the school house, to light them fires.'

In the woods, the elm and beech trees had by this time turned to pure gold. The oak was slowly changing to a deep bronze and the chestnut trees were full of flowing leaves of red and gold. On the ground below was a carpet of open burrs, all the acorns and conkers having disappeared.

As we gathered the kindling and made bundles of the dry twigs, around us the multicoloured leaves came fluttering down. We called out their names and their colours. We found new words for their movement – floating, twirling, twisting, drenching, raining, drifting, and we danced with the leaves.

'Do you wonder why they fall?'

'Why, miss?'

'Well all these trees are preparing for the spring. They know that they will need room for fresh new buds, so they force the old leaves to fall.'

'How do they do that, miss?'

'To live, we all need food, but the mother tree stops feeding them the sap that keeps them fresh and green. As the leaves change colour, they become dry and then the breezes blow them down easily and they cover the ground. But that's not the end of the story. Earthworms drag the dead leaves down to the earth and so the soil around the tree becomes rich to feed the tree once again.'

A nature outing of this kind was always an opportunity to stimulate language and free writing, but occasionally there are other benefits too – with trout from the river, blackberries from the hedgerow and dry twigs to light my fire!

On the farm the children helped with the harvesting of the root crops – turnips, swedes and potatoes, which were covered with straw and bracken to keep out the frost. On the hillside slopes the brown bracken was cut and hauled for bedding.

From the farms came the bleating of sheep as they were gathered together for the ewe sales. On the mountains the ponies and their foals were rounded up and counted. Some were taken to the horse fairs.

However, unlike the older boys who were no longer with us, these younger pupils were not kept away from school nor did they turn up in the mornings tired and dishevelled. Remembering some of the best days with those rough and ready boys, I had to admit I was missing them.

35

The first few weeks gave me the opportunity to organise my school work for the term so that when the time came for us to begin work in the house, I was free to do so. Every school day, when Mrs Staley's school chores were done, we'd 'get crackin'' or 'get our skates on' as she was wont to say.

Our handyman Len Jones kept us supplied with dry oak logs. The beech kindling would hiss and crackle on the range and in no time we had a roaring fire and there was always a kettle simmering on the hob.

In trousers, sweater and a turban to cover my hair, I followed Mrs Staley's instructions. We started in the scullery, first scraping and brushing off the loose bits on the walls and ceiling and then giving a white lime wash to the walls to kill off germs. The long wall built into the bank of the high garden which showed signs of green mildew was given an extra preservative treatment.

Then on to the other rooms, working together on the same task, sometimes on ladders, scraping, flaking, sanding, plastering and other times on our knees. Systematically, we worked through the living room, the parlour, the stairway and the bedrooms. Scraping and sanding the beams nearly killed me!

In the bedrooms where lining paper was covered with yellow distemper, we pulled off the paper in long sheets revealing cracks and holes. Where the holes near the skirtings were deep I had the bright idea of making use of the old plasticine balls I had discarded and would stuff it in, to fill the hole before plastering the surface with adamant.

November brought evenings when the storm raged and gusts of bitter wind rattled the windows and the wind went howling through the chimney pots. The broken shed door banged and clattered with monotonous rhythm but we pressed on regardless, working in the light of the Tilley lamp which threw shadows on the wall.

'I be needin' more light for this job, Mrs Thomas,' so standing on a chair I'd hold up a flickering candle and watch her on top of the step ladder energetically and cheerfully tackling the task in hand, always as bright as a button. I'd think to myself, never in my wildest dreams did I anticipate that I would be so blessed to find anyone like her.

So the evenings and weeks went by and the preparation of ceilings, walls and woodwork seemed never-ending. Dredged with the white dust that fell around us, we'd have a break to enjoy a much needed cup of tea. Then around nine o'clock we would wearily wend our way homeward in the deepening dusk. There were windy nights when the dark trees swayed with wildly tossing branches and we'd sally forth buffeted by the strong gale.

There were stormy nights when we got drenched by the swirling, driving rain, but there were also nights when the lovely wintry moon peeped through the white, fast-moving clouds and the landscape was transformed with silver light and eerie shadows.

It was on such a night that we came out from the back of the school house to the main schoolyard, and in the moonlight we could see at ground level, like a row of turnips, four round heads facing us beyond the wall.

'Wot the devil?' said Mrs Staley, walking towards the fence, but the whish-whoosh against the wall gave us the answer!

'Well, well it be another wet night, Mrs Thomas,' she chuckled and boisterous laughter followed us as we went on our way along the road.

There was always a large kettle of hot water on the hob and after a good wash in the kitchen, having discarded our working clothes, we'd sit in our dressing gowns and enjoy our supper; tired but always pleased with another day's work.

At last came the day when all the preparation was done. Everywhere was washed down with sugar soap and a coating of size put on walls and ceilings. We were now ready to start decorating and painting.

During my weekends and half term I had chosen wallpaper for all the rooms and enough undercoat and topcoat to cover all the woodwork in white. For the living room, we had rolls of apple green with white snowflake patterns; for the parlour, trailing ivy on a white background; for the stairway, white anaglypta. The children's bedroom was to have spring flowers in shades of blue and the main bedroom roses in shades of pink and white.

I had also purchased material in co-ordinating colours for curtains, which were being made at home.

'If you get on with the painting, Mrs Thomas, I'll soon see to the wallpaper.'

True to her word, the rolls went up like magic and there was not a line or bubble to be seen. As for the painting, she soon realised I was having problems whether on my knees doing the skirtings or on the step ladder painting the beams.

'Look out for them runs,' she'd say examining my handiwork.

Later in the canteen I heard her say to Jesse,

'If you got a spare hour, Jess, Mrs Thomas do need a hand with the paintin' with the gloss finish. She be gettin' more on herself, not bein' used to it like. We be needin' to get our skates on if we are to get 'er in for Christmas.'

'Sure to! Sure to!' said Jesse. 'I be with you, lass!'

36

December had arrived crisp and cheerful, the ground hard with frost and puddles and pools frozen. Shrubs and hedges had a new beauty in the clear frosty air and the birds that had stayed with us were flitting along the hedgerows.

In school we were beginning to prepare for Christmas, learning carols, preparing for a nativity play, making cards, calendars and paper decorations.

Mrs Staley had ordered the ingredients for a Christmas pudding and on the day the mixture was ready, up went the canteen hatch.

'Anyone who do want a stir for luck, come now!'

So we called in the infants and we all lined up to take our turn, stirring with a large wooden spoon.

We brought in a sturdy young fir tree with plenty of spreading branches and collected sprays of holly, glossy with leaves and thick with bright red berries.

We invited the governors to our nativity and Mrs Christie of Llangoed Hall came in a long black dress and coat and a large black Christie hat.

The schoolroom was full of Christmas cheer and after a delicious Christmas dinner with roast pork and all the trimmings we sang, 'Now we all want some Christmas pudding.'

She stood there in her white overall, red-cheeked, eyes sparkling and beaming with delight.

'Have all you children 'ad elegant sufficiency?' she asked – one of her favourite sayings after a good meal, and we all shouted 'Yes' and said, 'Three cheers for Mrs Staley. Hip Hip Hooray! Hip Hip Hooray! Hip Hip Hooray!'

So the Christmas term ended with our usual school chores which brought to an end my time as County Supply Teacher. It had been a difficult but memorable year but well worth the struggle.

On the last day a representative from Warwick Galleries called at the school. He had with him a collection of paintings, but the one that caught my eye was an original watercolour by Hughes Richardson – of a beautiful moorland in autumn. It brought to mind the wide open spaces of the Twmpath, covered with bracken in shades of yellow and russet brown.

Why not buy this painting to mark this special occasion, I thought? But then I noticed the price – £15, substantially more than my week's salary! It would be irresponsible of me to spend so much, when every penny was needed to furnish the school house.

During the preceding weeks I had purchased all the main items but there were still household items to be bought and very little money left.

'I have several satisfied customers all over Wales,' he said.

'Yes, my father is one of them. He bought Priddey's Pembroke Castle and Manorbier Castle from you.'

He beamed with pleasure.

Mrs Staley came in with a cup of Camp. She eyed the paintings.

'One of they would be just right for that space above the grate in the parlour, Mrs Thomas.'

He drank his cup of coffee, waiting for my decision. I still hesitated. It would be so extravagant! – but my salary cheque had arrived that morning, and I could buy myself a Christmas present, couldn't I . . . ?

After he had gone I showed the painting to Mrs Staley.

'It be a real nice picture,' she said.

'I paid fifteen,' I said.

'Well fifteen bob won't break you, gel! It be a bargain, I reckon!'

I dare not tell her, I thought. She'll think I've gone off my top!

Throughout the years that painting was to bring back many happy memories and there came a day thirty years later when it was to be valued for five hundred pounds.

37

We had worked incessantly throughout those first two weeks in December. Jesse took over the painting and Mrs Staley finished the wall papering. By the end of term the last-minute cleaning was done and the whole house was sparkling.

We broke up on the 18th and that gave me enough time to have everything delivered and in order before the family arrived on the 23rd.

Every firm had received strict instructions as to dates and times of delivery so there should be no delay.

I had decided not to move in until curtains were up, beds were made and there was a place for everything and everything in its place. So during the day, I worked in the house and every night I spent with Mrs Staley.

I'd had to start from scratch. I had not even asked for any of my former possessions which were still in storage in Bristol. They would have brought too many poignant memories.

However, different members of my family had been generous in providing sheets, blankets, towels, and a very pretty set of willow pattern china which would look very attractive on the shelves, which Jesse had erected in my whitewashed pantry.

Every task was a joy and gave me such pleasure and satisfaction. It seemed to me that I knew every corner, every part of this little school house, and on that last night, as I wandered from room to room I was overwhelmed with excitement, anticipating the children's reaction to this new home. In the glow of the lamp in my hand, everywhere looked so comfortable and inviting. I had no doubt that it would be considered primitive by many, without electricity, hot water and having a privy down the yard, but to me it was a little palace.

I walked through the village in high spirits and there was more good news. The friendly young girl chatting to Mrs Staley was waiting for me. She had heard that I was looking for someone to look after Lynne during school days. Her name was Eileen and she lived on a farm, a few miles away. I took a liking to her immediately and in no time we had come to an agreement and arranged that she would live in from Monday to Friday. This was better than I had expected and indeed Eileen turned out to be a treasure and Sharon and Lynne loved her.

'Providence be smilin' on you, Mrs Thomas,' Mrs Staley said as we sat down to supper.

'I just can't believe that everything is going so well,' I said.

'This news is the icing on the cake, but I could never have done it without you, Mrs Staley. I owe you so much! No amount of money will repay you for your support and enthusiasm but I hope you'll get together with Jesse. I want to settle with you both before Christmas for all your hours of hard work.'

'Now listen to me, Mrs Thomas, Jesse and me be of the same mind. We don't want no money. It 'ave given us a lift of 'eart to 'elp and it be reward enough to see you settled in the school house with your little 'uns.'

She saw that I was near to tears.

'Now off you go to bed. You look fair wore out.'

So for the last time I went up 'the wooden 'ill' to the little bedroom and as always the glow from the candle illuminated the text on the wall.

God is our shelter and strength
Always ready to help in times of trouble.

38

Morning came and it was the beginning of a very busy day. A local farm provided a fourteen-pound turkey, Welsh butter and eggs; Ray the Stores delivered groceries, vegetables, fruit and other Christmas fare, which included Christmas crackers and decorations. Len Jones brought in the holly and a small fir tree, and I spent the afternoon decorating the parlour and the Christmas tree.

The ivy patterned wallpaper, the white paintwork that set off the regency curtains, and the red tiled Victorian grate formed a colourful setting for the greenery and sparkling decorations and I was pleased with my handiwork.

Mrs Staley was expecting her family for Christmas but she managed to come down for a sherry, to celebrate.

'It do look a treat gel,' she said as she went from room to room. Your mam, dad and the little 'uns will be over the moon, I reckon!'

'Yes, they'll be here tomorrow and they are looking forward to meeting you and to thank you for everything you have done for me.'

Later, Jesse called. 'By damn!' he said standing in the doorway, hands in breeches and his flat cap perched on his untidy corn-coloured locks. There was a look of surprise on his rugged 'Popeye' face.

'I be proper flabbergasted,' as he viewed every room.

Of course, it had been a week since he had called and at that time the house was empty, so there had been a transformation.

'I am very grateful to you for everything you have done, Jesse, and I still owe you for all the hours you've spent painting, so please let me have the bill.'

He shook his head and looked embarrassed.

'You did pay me for all the jobs I done. I did the paintin' to help you out and I don't want no money for that, so we be

142

quits, I reckon. Anyrod I be glad to do it. My missus be wonderin' w'ere I got to, so I'll be sayin' Merry Christmas, Mrs Thomas!' And off he went.

I drew the curtains, shutting out the weather and without lighting the oil lamp, I sat in the bright glow of the fire. The red and yellow flames danced and caressed the dry logs and the blue-black smoke drifted up the chimney, filling the air with an aromatic smell of burning wood. I relaxed sleepily, thinking that there was no comfort like the warmth of a wood fire.

From my armchair, the richness of the dark oak furniture showed up against the russet carpet and the apple green wallpaper, and the blue and gold Welsh lustre jugs glowed on the bureau.

This then was my first evening in my new home. Who was it who said, 'This is the first day of the rest of my life?'

Yes, I had accepted that the way ahead would be lonely. In the world I knew, marriage was for ever. I had no doubt that there had always been some unhappy marriages but I knew of no couple who had chosen to part, or any wife and children abandoned, as in our case. Divorce was not even a word accepted in our vocabulary. I faced a future where all decisions would be mine; one of my deliberate choosing. I saw no possibility of ever having another relationship.

The die was cast and there was no turning back.

EPILOGUE
1980

I drove through the main gateway of the Old Vicarage. The lazy purr-purr coos of the turtle doves in the tall pine trees greeted me as I fumbled the key into the keyhole and entered the spacious hall with its lofty ceiling and elegant staircase. It was a far cry from that little school house which had been our home for seven years.

I had remarried and in 1960 my husband Brian Winfield had brought us to the Midlands and taken on the role of father to Sharon and Lynne and, by now, grandfather to Marie, Louise, Gareth and Ceri Anne.

During the past two years we had lived in this beautiful Victorian rectory which my husband had restored to its former glory.

I made my way to the large oak kitchen and felt the warmth from the Rayburn. I made myself a cup of tea and carried it into the study. I stood deep in thought looking out at the garden full of shrubs and trees, the woodland carpeted with wild daffodils and clusters of yellow and purple crocuses.

Normally the long journey from school to home gave me the opportunity to unwind from the daily pressures of school but today my thoughts had been far away in Gwenddwr.

In that isolated village, the children and I had found a refuge which, despite the loneliness, had brought a period of stability, happiness and exciting challenge. Without Mrs Staley's constant support and encouragement, it would have been a far greater hurdle.

She would be greatly mourned by all who knew her.

Kahlil Gibran wrote:

> There are those who have little and give it all
> These are the believers in life and the bounty of life
> And their coffer is never empty.

This memorable quotation is a fitting tribute to a very special person and a truly memorable friend.